Leckie ✕ Leckie

HIGHER
Product Design
course notes

David McMillan ✕ Donald Stewart

This book is dedicated to all the pupils we have taught this course to
over the last twenty years and who never had the benefit of this book.
Some are now practising designers and we are proud of them.

ISBN 978-1-84372-183-3

Published by
Leckie & Leckie Ltd, 3rd floor, 4 Queen Street, Edinburgh, EH2 1JE
Tel: 0131 220 6831 Fax: 0131 225 9987
enquiries@leckieandleckie.co.uk   www.leckieandleckie.co.uk

Edited by
The Partnership Publishing Solutions Ltd www.the-pps.co.uk

Special thanks to
Tom Davie, Eleanor Jackson, Mark Leishman, Susan McLaren, Neil Walker, James Young High
School, Livingston

Mind Maps® is a registered trademark of the Buzan Organisation.
Tony Buzan is the originator of Mind Maps.

Leckie & Leckie is grateful for the following for their permission to reproduce their material:
Motoring Picture Library/Alamy (p65 & p67); Carphotos/Alamy(p67); Smart (p67);
Barry Perks (p69); Hugh Threlfall/Alamy (p71); Arcaid/Alamy (p92 & p157); Tefal (p92); The
Bridgewater Book Company (p94); Sony (p95); Michele De Lucchi (p110);
BMW (p116 & p117); Image Source/Alamy (p121); Graham Hearn (p137); Almo Office (p148);
John Makepeace Furniture (p173); Elizabeth Whiting & Associates/Alamy (p176); Thonet (p176);
IKEA (p178); The Co-Op group (p184); The Glasgow Arts School (p190); IBRAE (p202)

A CIP Catalogue record for this book is available from the British Library.

Leckie & Leckie Ltd is a division of Huveaux plc.

Contents

Section 3: Practice

INTRODUCTION

This book has been written to support your work in Higher Grade and Intermediate 2 Product Design. It will also assist you with your revision for the written examination that you will sit at the end of the course. Each double page covers one topic, which can be read on its own or in conjunction with other related topics. This should help you to find information easily and plan your own revision. Although the book has been divided into three sections it is clear that some topics could appear in more than one. So to fully understand the process of designing and some of the many complex issues a designer must face you should read the whole book.

No attempt has been made to show you how to design. Designing is something that will be unique to each school and to each pupil. Creating and generating ideas can be done in many different ways. Sketching, drawing, modelling, evaluating and decision making are all activities that need to be explored and worked at individually and it is important that you develop your own way of doing this if you are to have your own design style. This book attempts to guide you through the process of designing. It highlights some of the main areas for research work as well as some of the main restrictions and constraints a designer will face.

How to use this book

Throughout the book you will find several case studies which will ask you to visit a web site and carry out a task. This is designed to help you to broaden your knowledge and experience of products and companies as well as becoming more familiar with the work of practising designers. Carry out these tasks and keep your work in a separate file alongside your answers to the questions in the 'Revise as you go' sections which are in each topic. You will find interesting web links in most of these sites. Take the time to explore these and remember to add examples of good design to your file along with any interesting and relevant facts that you discover. Whilst online, keep an eye on the Leckie & Leckie website for further Higher Product Design resources and web links. Simply visit **www.leckieandleckie.co.uk** and click on the *Learning Lab* button. The book should also help you to understand what is taught in class as well as helping you to manage your own design work.

Assessment

The final examination paper at Higher Grade will be 2 hours long. You will have the opportunity to work on examination topics during your coursework but don't leave it too late. The questions set in the 'Revise as you go' section are similar in nature to those you will have to answer in the final examination. Revise as you go throughout the course. Remember to add your answers to your file. Your teacher will also set you extended design projects which will require you to put the knowledge gained from this book into practice. You will then be given a Design Assignment to do later in the year which will be sent away for marking and will contribute to your final award.

SECTION 1
Process

Section 1: Process

The Design Process

There are many models that can be used to describe the design process. All have merit and it would be wrong to say that one model should be used in preference to another. What is important is to realise that a design team will progress through a series of stages towards a final proposal. Throughout these stages, the design team should consult the client and consumer – through continuous evaluation, previous stages can be revisited and updated or changed as required. The model below shows one such process and illustrates some of the inputs that can be made by the client/consumer and the design team.

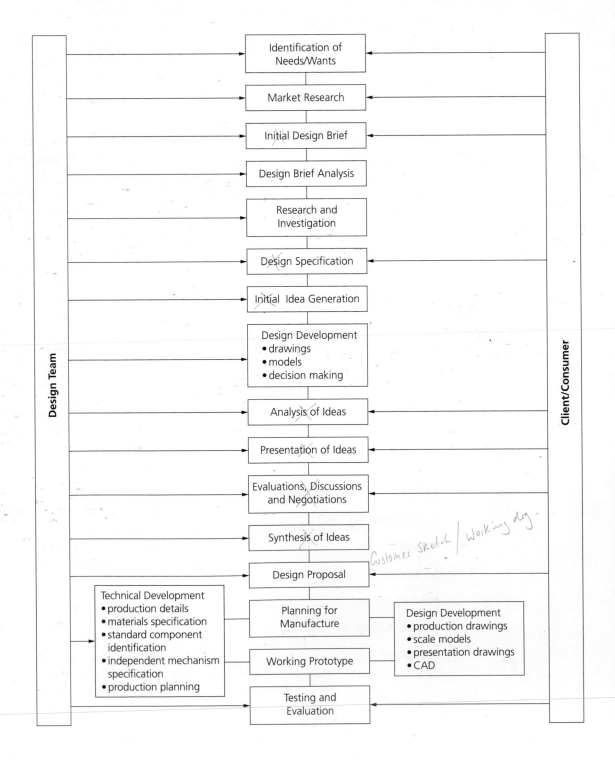

Revise as you go!

- *To which stages in the design process is the client able to make a contribution?*
- *Describe briefly the contribution the client is able to make at each of these stages.*

This model only gives a flavour of the type of work and some of the activities involved in designing products. It is a very linear model, which in fact rarely applies in such a rigid form when a designer is involved in design activity. For example, the process of evaluation is ongoing and can be applied to every stage; designers will constantly evaluate early ideas against their specification before developing the best ones further. The specification must also be evaluated and compared with the results of any market research work that has been undertaken to ensure that the criteria for the proposed solution meet the needs and expectations of the client and the end user. Even the process of planning for manufacture need not wait until the creative work has been completed. There is a lot of discussion, investigation and questions about this that can be answered during the early stages of the project.

The model shown is a logical and methodical way of looking at the design process. Putting these activities in that order makes it easy to explain and doing things in that sequence can be justified. However, design is a human activity undertaken by creative people who are striving to be original, so they may often break away from such conventional methods. It may be more helpful to consider the process of designing as having three stages which, if the designer feels it appropriate, can be done in any order.

Research and Investigation	Idea Development and Communicating Ideas	Presenting Proposals and Preparing for Manufacture

These three stages can be compared to the beginning, middle and end of a book and although the reader will read the book in that order it does not mean that it was written that way. The activities undertaken at each of the three stages are varied and will depend on factors such as who the product is for, what timescale is involved, manufacturing restrictions and cost. Throughout the process the designer will have discussions with relevant people, work independently to tight deadlines, write out proposals, and sketch ideas and model solutions. Their communication skills will be tested to the limit and they will be involved in evaluative, analytical and creative thinking at each of these three stages.

The process of designing is unique to each designer. We all do it differently and deal with unexpected situations and unforeseen problems in our own way. At some point we will all experience each of the activities in the linear model shown, but it is our ability to cope, make decisions and be creative at each stage that determines whether or not the products that we design are successful.

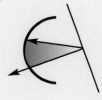

Case Study

There are many models of the design process that can be used to illustrate the process of design. Visit **www.ider.herts.ac.uk/school/courseware/design/** and make notes which you can add to your file on communicating ideas, ergonomics, materials, manufacturing and marketing.

The Design Team

Before the industrial revolution, most products were made using handcraft technologies. Marketplaces were fairly restricted and manufacturers were able to respond to much more specific customer needs. In most cases, there was a direct relationship between the manufacturers and the purchasers. Products took time to make, some being made to order. This had the advantage that products could be altered or customised to suit individual needs.

Today, it is likely that designers will have to respond to more generalised consumer markets than to specific ones with restricted briefs.

Products now have to compete in much wider marketplaces and most commercially manufactured items are mass produced. They are usually the result of quite extensive developments in materials, systems technologies and production methods. The more complex nature of modern products has made it impossible for any single designer to work on his or her own. Most designers now work as part of bigger teams, liaising with other experts from time to time.

The diagram below gives an indication of the type of experts who may be asked to contribute to a design team.

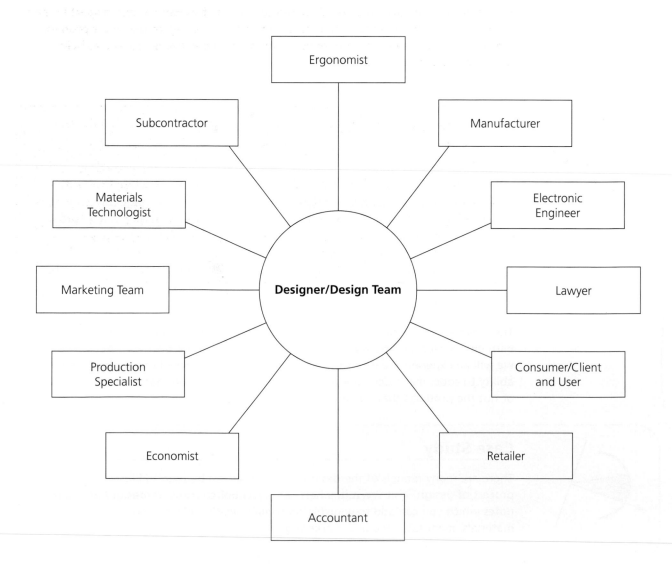

Designers themselves will usually have some expertise in each of these areas but will find it difficult to keep up to date with new developments because of the specialised nature of each. For example, recent developments in rapid prototyping have meant that more accurate and detailed models and prototypes can be produced quickly. In-house rapid prototyping is relatively rare since it requires expensive, specialist equipment. Design studios will often use bureaux or 'hubs' to provide modelling when they need it; this allows them to choose from all types of rapid prototyping processes to suit specific modelling needs.

Designers must also liaise closely with the people who make the moulds for their product. Their knowledge and experience is vital in ensuring that expensive mistakes are avoided during the manufacturing process. They will spend time with the designer discussing their drawings and models. Together they will examine details such as wall thickness for plastic, angle for tapers to allow the product to be withdrawn from the mould, injection points, strengthening ribs and webs, and location points as well as the overall complexity and cost of making the mould.

The marketing team, proposed retailers and selected consumer groups may well be asked to comment on proposed products by examining and testing models and prototypes and presentation visuals. Their feedback will be useful and may prompt changes to the product before going to final production.

In general any designer must be prepared to work with others who are expert in their own field. Their knowledge should be used to help the designer develop a product which is cheaper, more efficient, easier to manufacture and safer, as well as being easier to use and more marketable.

Revise as you go!

- *Write down how you feel each of the 'experts' shown in the diagram might help the designer.*
- *Choose two of these experts and describe how they would keep their expertise up to date.*
- *The success of any design team depends on good communication. List six methods of communication members of a design team could use to communicate with each other.*

The Design Brief

Usually, the starting point for the design of a new product is the design brief. This brief will indicate the general nature of the task or problem to be solved and usually does not impose very tight definitions or unnecessary restrictions. If the problem is specified exactly then the solution to it may become obvious and there are fewer opportunities for creative thinking, innovation or indeed invention. So, as the name suggests, the information and instructions given are often very **'brief'**.

The design brief can be used as a starting point for much research and discussion, which in turn will lead to the writing of a full specification. It is often seen as an intermediate stage between the initial idea for a product and the writing of the specification.

The design brief should contain sufficient information to establish the **design goal**, the **major constraints** within which this goal must be achieved and some **criteria** by which a good design solution can be recognised.

The design brief can be written by anyone, but the client, consumer and designer usually discuss its suitability. This should establish whether there is a need or desire for a specific solution.

In general terms design briefs fall into two categories: the open brief and the closed brief.

Open Brief

This can be defined as a brief which sets out what has to be done in fairly general terms. Many things are left open to interpretation and a wide range of possible solutions may be acceptable. Obviously, this makes it possible to propose truly original solutions but has the disadvantage that much time and money can be wasted producing a solution that may be unacceptable to the client.

Example

Design a product that tells the time.

The first product that springs to mind is a clock. But is it a digital clock or a clock with hands? Should it be wall mounted or freestanding? Is it to be used indoors or outdoors? There are many more specific things that need to be considered if indeed a clock is the direction the product is to take. However consider a sundial, a candle, a wristwatch or even a recorded voice that speaks the time. These are all solutions that answer the brief. All have a different function and are designed for different environments and different markets. Is the brief that has been set too open?

Closed Brief

A closed brief is much more specific and will direct the designer towards what the client wants. Here the client has greater control, which may restrict the designer from producing innovative solutions.

Example

Design a wall-mounted clock in the style of Charles Rennie Mackintosh for a family living room. The finished product should package flat into an A3 cardboard box and retail for around £20.00.

It is clear that the opportunities for developing an innovative solution are very restricted. The function, style and size of the product have already been defined. A digital clock is unlikely to satisfy the brief so the only real creative input the designer can make is to experiment with the styling and appearance based around Mackintosh features.

The need for discussion between the client and designer is clear. The design brief should highlight major restrictions and identify areas for research. As a result of this discussion and research, the design specification will evolve.

Every design brief can be written in a different way and it would be wrong to say that one particular style is better than any other. There is no formula or single method that is used to write a brief and the type of information contained in each will depend on the requirements of the client and the design team. Issues involving manufacture, expected sales, proposed retail outlets, market group and product life expectancy must also play a part in the early stages to enable the design team to establish a direction for their research and development work.

Revise as you go!
- *Explain the difference between a 'closed brief' and an 'open brief'.*
- *What type of information is likely to be exchanged between a designer and a client when the design brief is being discussed?*

Design Brief Analysis

A design brief is usually the start of the design process – it gives the designer an indication of what is to be done. After careful analysis, it should also direct the designer towards areas of importance which should be investigated and researched. It is difficult to specify a range of tasks or activities that should be carried out for every design brief because these tasks will vary with each brief. It is better to think about the design brief analysis as being a process that will ensure that the designer is as informed as possible about problems, restrictions and other areas of importance that may influence the final product.

To begin the analysis of the brief, it may help to ask these four questions.

- Are there any **economic** restrictions or demands?
- What are the **functional** restrictions and demands?
- What **aesthetic** considerations must be made?
- What effects and consequences will any proposed solution have on the **environment**?

Each of these four areas can be thought of as headings and examined further as shown below. The topics under each heading can act as a guide for further investigation but should not be regarded as a definitive list, nor are they given in order of priority.

Function	Aesthetics	Economics	Environment
Strength	Shape	Time	Sustainability
Structure	Colour	Resources	Waste
Stability	Proportion	Equipment	Recycling
Material	Form	Skills	Reuse
Ergonomics	Contrast	Volume	Repair
Size	Texture	Material	Global Issues
Durability	Line	Market Needs	Consequences
Use	Balance	Production	Pollution
Maintenance	Style	Finance	Material
Shape	Material		Local Environment
Construction	Target Market		Personal Environment
			Resources
			Workforce
			Transportation

Other specific areas such as **value for money, ease of maintenance, running costs** and **fitness for purpose** must also be considered at an early stage. All of these headings should generate much discussion and will result in an in-depth examination of the main design issues. Information can be collected from many sources, such as books, journals, surveys, electronic media and existing products. As a result of this analysis and research work, the writing of the design specification can begin. This work, if done well, will prepare the designer more fully for the task ahead.

Consider the following analysis written by a fifth year pupil who was asked to design a hairdryer for males aged between 16 and 25 years old.

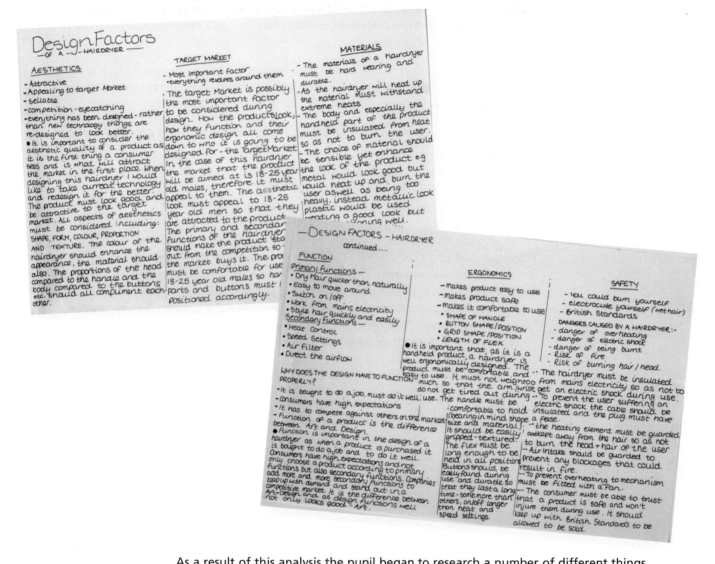

As a result of this analysis the pupil began to research a number of different things. Four of her research tasks are listed below.

■ Produce a lifestyle board and research images and products that appeal to males aged between 16 and 25 years old.

■ Research materials already used in the production of hairdryers and find out about safety regulations that must be observed.

■ Examine existing hairdryers and find out which features and functions are included.

■ Experiment with hand-held products and record which products are comfortable to hold. Collect appropriate anthropometric data.

Revise as you go!

● *Explain how writing out a design brief analysis can help with writing a specification.*

● *How could the client help the designer with the design brief analysis?*

Market Research

Research is a very time-consuming activity that is often seen as being an unglamorous part of a designer's work. However market research has a very important part to play in the development of any new product.

Deciding which market to aim a new product at is vital to its success. Before making such a decision, designers and companies often consult other sources of information which have already been published. This information can show:

- whether the total market for a particular product or service is growing, static or declining
- what changes are taking place in the market in which the product will be competing
- who will be the main competitors to the product.

Market research is carried out to try to reduce the risk and uncertainty surrounding the development of a new product. There are two basic types of research techniques: **field research** and **desk research**. To carry out effective and meaningful field research the designer must have a clear understanding of the type of information required. If the wrong questions are asked of the wrong people then the answers and information given will be useless. Desk research is not always so specific an activity. It can involve hours of sifting through existing information that has perhaps been collated for another reason.

Field Research

- **Experiments** – such as demonstrating a new product in a store after its launch
- **Audits** – carrying out a check of product stock in shops and stores
- **Observing** – such as noting how many people use a public telephone over a set period
- **Recording** – counting how often consumers use a specific product over a set time
- **Surveys** – interaction with a specified market group through questionnaires, individual interviews and group interviews

Desk Research

- **External sources** – reports, newspapers, journals, media reports, government audits
- **Internal sources** – accounts, sales records

Desk research may not always provide the most up-to-date information. The fact that the source has already been published may mean that current trends or new competition to the product have not been taken into account. However, it may well provide general information about consumers and competitors. It is much cheaper and quicker to undertake than field research because the information has already been recorded. For this reason it is usually undertaken first.

Asking questions from a sample of people within a specific market group can provide useful information.

Establishing who the target market is before beginning any research is vital. It is clear that for all commercially produced products collecting information from everyone in the chosen group will prove impossible. However it should be possible to study a **sample** of this group. Before starting this study three things must have been decided.

1   **How are the people in the survey to be chosen?**
    This should be considered carefully as surveying family and friends who belong to the chosen group may not provide a representative view.

2   **Who is to be surveyed?**
    Should it only be those in the market group that should be considered or could others provide useful information? For example parents' views should be considered when designing products for children.

3   **How many people should be surveyed?**
    Large samples clearly provide more information than small samples. The problem is knowing when to stop. There is a danger that market research activities could go on forever in the hope that something might be found that creates a stimulus that gives your product the edge over the competition.

Revise as you go!

- *A company is designing a new vacuum cleaner and wishes to carry out some market research. Describe the type of information that can be found out by (a) observing end users (b) questioning consumers and (c) examining other similar products.*

- *What type of work is normally carried out using desk research?*

Specifications

Specifications are statements of the characteristics a design must possess in order to meet the requirements of the design brief. A full design specification will contain a lot of highly technical information and requirements, as well as other less technical requirements. It is therefore quite common to distinguish between a marketing specification, a technical specification, a performance specification and a conformance specification.

- **Marketing specification** (*Will it sell?*)

  This emphasises the requirements of the user, the purchaser and the producing company, e.g. user groups, price, product life, maintenance, materials, production timescale, manufacturing methods and function.

- **Technical specification** (*Can it be made?*)

  This translates some of the requirements in the marketing specification into precise descriptions, setting limits as well as giving values and measurements. It deals with the more physical properties of the product, e.g. power ratings, dimensions and essential properties of materials.

- **Performance specification** (*Will it work?*)

  This deals with the desired outputs of a product, e.g. what function it must fulfil, ease of use by a range of people, how well the product performs in different environments, how durable and robust the product is or how safe the product is when in use.

- **Conformance specification** (*Is it safe and legal?*)

  This should ensure that the product complies with legal and commercial requirements and that it is safe to use by the public. Things like British standards, industry standards, statutory requirements and intellectual property rights must all be observed.

A coherent product specification is important because it sets out clear boundaries within which the designer must work. However, a specification that is too restrictive may prevent the investigation of a much wider range of acceptable solutions.

An example of an inappropriate specification would be to say at the outset of a project that a kitchen work surface should be made of Formica® when the only restrictions given in the **performance** criteria are that the surface should have a smooth texture, be resistant to knocks and be easy to clean. Clearly, Formica meets these criteria but so do a range of other materials. However, there may be many other desired attributes for this work surface in the **market** and **technical** requirements such as overall size, thickness, aesthetics and cost. These may lead to Formica being selected as the most appropriate material.

It can be a mistake to try to decide on the specification too quickly. In most cases, there is a need for some interaction between writing the specification and generating design ideas. Many details of the specification will depend upon suggested ideas.

Writing a specification takes time and effort, and involves research into the needs and requirements of users, buyers, retailers and manufacturers. It is useful to consider the product requirements for each of these groups under the following headings before writing specifications:

- ◆ Performance
- ◆ Safety
- ◆ Ergonomics
- ◆ Ease of use
- ◆ Materials
- ◆ Aesthetics
- ◆ Function
- ◆ Marketing
- ◆ Manufacture

The aim of any specification is to try and establish what things could cause a new product to fail. It provides an opportunity for the designer to specify targets or set down rules to avoid the product being unsafe, unpopular, difficult to use or inappropriate in any way.

The design specification sets out criteria which are part of a key quality control document for the finished product. It clearly sets out what the product must and should do and is a useful tool for the design team to ensure that nothing is left out during the designing and development stages.

However, the specification is likely to evolve as the idea moves through the design, research, development and modelling phases.

Bigger Picture

The following is part of a specification written by a fifth year pupil who was asked to design a hairdryer for Alessi. This excerpt shows examples of performance, market, technical and conformance requirements.

Specification
- DESIGN -

- THE DESIGN MUST DRY HAIR EFFICIENTLY USING AN EXISTING POWER SOURCE
- THE DESIGN MUST PRODUCE 2000W OF POWER AC 220/240 V
- THE DESIGN MUST PRODUCE A FLOW OF HOT AIR THAT CAN BE CONTROLLED AND REGULATED
- THE DESIGN MUST BE COMFORTABLE TO HOLD FOR BOTH LEFT AND RIGHT HANDED USERS
- THE PRODUCT WILL BE DESIGNED FOR EASY OPERATION WITH ONE HAND.
- THE DESIGN MUST BE LIGHTWEIGHT FOR EASE OF USE - BETWEEN 350 and 700 g.
- THE DESIGN MUST BE EASY TO CLEAN WITHOUT WATER OR DETERGENTS
- THE BODY OF THE PRODUCT MUST BE INSULATED FROM HEAT AND ELECTRICITY
- THE PRODUCT MUST BE FITTED WITH A PROTECTION SYSTEM TO PREVENT WARE AT CONNECTION POINTS
- THE MATERIALS MUST BE HEAT PROOF
- THE PRODUCT MUST BE DOUBLE INSULATED
- THE PRODUCT MUST PREVENT HAIR FROM BEING CAUGHT OR TRAPPED
- THE PRODUCT WILL APPEAL TO THE 16-25 yrold MALE
- THE PRODUCT WILL HAVE A STRONG IMAGE
- THE PRODUCT WILL BE MASS PRODUCED USING VARIOUS MANUFACTURING TECHNIQUES APPROPRIATE TO THE PERFORMANCE, FINANCIAL CONSTRAINTS, QUALITY AND AESTHETICS.
- THE PRODUCT WILL BE DEVELOPED AROUND EXISTING STANDARD COMPONANTS TO ENSURE RELIABILITY AND COMPETITIVENESS IN THE MARKET PLACE.
- THE PRODUCT MUST HAVE A REPLACABLE FUSE
- THE PRODUCT SHOULD HAVE A REMOVABLE FILTER FOR EASY CLEANING
- THE PRODUCT SHOULD BE TAMPERPROOF.
- THE DESIGN MUST BE MASS PRODUCED TO PROVIDE 600,000 UNITS
- THE PRODUCT SHOULD BE CONSTRUCTED FROM A LIMITED NUMBER OF PARTS
- THE DESIGN MUST BE EASY TO ASSEMBLE
- THE ASSEMBLY OF PARTS INCLUDING STANDARD COMPONANTS SHOULD BE SIMPLE AND REQUIRE A LOW SKILL LEVEL, COMPRESSION FITTING WOULD BE DESIRABLE.
- THE DESIGN SHOULD BE ENVIRONMENTALLY FRIENDLY.

Revise as you go!
- Write down five things you would include in the specification for a domestic iron.
- What type of information would you expect to find in a technical specification?

Researching Information

Research is vital to the success of every designer's work. Sourcing relevant information, collecting materials, identifying the important data and then using it can be a time-consuming activity. However, it is a necessary activity if the product is to succeed in today's highly competitive marketplace.

Before starting any kind of research activity it is worthwhile discussing with someone what information should be found out and why this information is needed. Knowing that the information you are researching will be used and having some understanding of what it will be used for will give added meaning to this time-consuming work. Setting out clear tasks at the beginning of a project will save time and give direction to the activities undertaken.

Asking questions will feature prominently in all types of research work. There is a skill to asking questions, and asking the right type of question of the right people is a key feature to collecting relevant data.

Essentially there are four different types of questions that can be asked.

■ **Closed Questions**

These usually result in a yes or no type of answer being given. Although this is useful, this type of question usually leads to the least amount of information being given.

■ **Open Questions**

This type of question is designed to encourage people to give their opinion or point of view. Open questions can be very difficult questions to ask and should be phrased carefully to avoid the risk of influencing any answer that might be given.

■ **Ratings Questions**

This type of question can also help people express an opinion and is a quicker and easier method than the open-ended question. People are normally asked to give a rating using a pre-determined scale of, say, 1 to 10.

■ **Structured Questions**

These are very useful particularly if answers may not be straightforward or a lot of information is required about something. It will prevent people going off at a tangent and giving long-winded answers which are not necessary.

There are two main types of research work that can be undertaken. These can be termed '**primary research**' and '**secondary research**'.

The computer is now an essential part of research work. It can be used to prepare questionnaires, set up web pages and provide simulations; as well as giving access to the web.

Primary Research

This involves doing the work oneself and often requires the designer to travel, interview people and visit certain locations. Examples include:

- making direct contact with recognised experts and interviewing them
- doing some form of fieldwork and collecting data
- keeping in contact with the client
- testing models and other similar commercially-produced products
- visiting exhibitions, displays and trade shows to collect information
- producing questionnaires and carrying out surveys
- modelling and conducting computer simulations and analysing the results.

Secondary Research

This type of research is usually much easier and involves using the results of other people's primary research. Examples include:

- reading articles from books, magazines and journals
- accessing the Internet
- collecting product literature produced by the manufacturer/designer
- reading handout sheets, data sheets, consumer reports.

Throughout the process of researching and collating data, it is important that the information gained is kept in an organised state and that only the useful and relevant parts of this information are used. Usually only a small percentage of the information collected is useful and designers must be careful not to waste time working with irrelevant data. Knowing what to include and what to leave out requires skill and judgement. Only information that will influence the design should be included in a portfolio. It can be used to support any decisions made during the design stages.

Revise as you go!
- *Explain the difference between a closed question and an open one.*
- *What types of activity are normally carried out doing primary research?*

Design Development Considerations

Although there are no rules for developing ideas, it is useful to be aware of the main factors that influence a designer's thinking, and of how concentrating on developing one area too much will affect the other areas.

Product design can be thought of as having four main issues which the designer must consider throughout the development process:

- **Functional Requirements**

  These will include factors like product performance, fitness for purpose, human interaction, ease of use, safety and reliability.

- **Aesthetic Requirements**

  Particular areas of interest will include intended market group, styling, market trends and product semantics.

- **Economic Constraints**

  This really concerns how resources are used and managed. For example what type of production is to be used, costs, available time, subcontracting, standard components and standardisation of parts. The designer also needs to be aware of product life strategy, obsolescence and future trends.

- **Environmental Concerns and Design for Sustainability**

  Designers have a moral duty to consider the environmental effects of their work. The use of sustainable materials, the pollution and waste generated through manufacturing, how the product will affect the environment it is to be used in, and recycling, are all important issues that need consideration.

It is possible to divide each of these four headings into specific topics that can be considered in depth during the process of developing a design idea. These individual topics will contribute to the evaluation of any proposed solution. They may also help in writing the design specification. For example:

Function	Aesthetics	Economics	Environment
Strength	Shape	Time	Waste
Structure	Colour	Resources	Recycling
Stability	Proportion	Equipment	Reuse
Material	Form	Skills	Repair
Ergonomics	Contrast	Volume	Global Issues
Size	Texture	Material	Consequences
Durability	Line	Market Needs	Pollution
Use	Balance	Production	Material
Maintenance	Style	Finance	Local Environment
Shape	Material		Personal Environment
Construction	Target Market		Resources

Many other things could be added to each list. However, the above range gives an indication of the type of aspects which may be considered under each of the four headings. It should also be noted that each topic is not restricted to one list only. For example, 'Material' appears in all four lists but should be considered differently in each.

Generating ideas and developing them is a gradual process. Each time a change is made it needs to be evaluated, then another change can be made and it can be evaluated again, and so on. However, when evaluating each change or improvement it is important to consider how it has affected the whole design. For example, if someone designed a dining room chair to be sold by a large retail company and only concentrated on its appearance then it is unlikely that the chair would be a commercial success. The finished product may look good but it also needs to be strong enough for an adult to sit in, as well as comfortable, stable, able to be mass produced and made from a sustainable material, and so on. The idea may look stunning but it has to do more.

The diagram shows how too much attention and focus given to the aesthetic qualities of a product may put a strain on the other three elements. Designers should be aware of how each of these four elements respond to any change that is made. None of these elements should be neglected. This is not to suggest that design is always a compromise but, where the focus of a design is obviously towards one of these elements, then the designer should be aware of the effect it will have on each of the others.

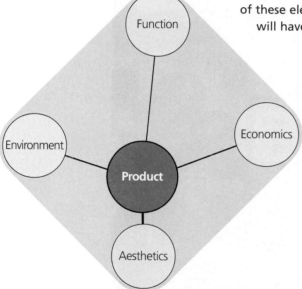

Revise as you go!

- *In the design of a new vacuum cleaner the designer only concentrates on the functional aspects. How is this likely to affect*
  - *(a) the way the product looks*
  - *(b) how the product affects the environment*
  - *(c) the overall cost of the product?*

- *Describe briefly how neglecting these three areas could affect sales of the vacuum cleaner.*

Lifestyle Board

Producing a lifestyle board can be a very easy way of giving a designer an aesthetic direction for a product. It should be full of visual images which give a snapshot of the lifestyle of the intended target market group. There are no rules for producing a lifestyle board but it is useful if certain guidelines are followed so that the information gained from the board can be used in a meaningful way.

1   The first and most obvious requirement is to identify the intended market group and then find out as much information about them as possible, e.g. age range, sex, socioeconomic group, culture and hobbies. Try to target more than one group. Do not assume that the product will appeal to only one type of customer. Few mass-produced products could survive with such a small customer base.

2   The next step can be more difficult and, if done properly, involves 'people watching'. The purpose of this is to get a general picture of this market group, where they go, what they wear, what food they eat and other relevant observations. Each person is different in these respects so it is necessary to establish areas that are common to them all.

A lifestyle board for an outgoing 18-year-old.

This should give an overall impression of their lifestyle, which should then be captured on a single lifestyle board.

The way this is done is to collect visual images of this market group's perceived lifestyle, such as:

■   the food they eat
■   the clothes they wear
■   where they go on holiday
■   the houses they live in
■   the cars they drive

- the music groups they listen to
- the leisure activities they undertake
- the styles of furniture they have in their homes
- the products they own and aspire to own.

These visual images can be taken from magazines, photographs, brochures or movies and may even include textiles and fabrics. The result should be a visual snapshot of the intended market group's life.

The designer can use the colours, shapes, patterns and styles found in the lifestyle board when designing a product. This can be described as giving the product an aesthetic direction. One of the evaluation tests that could be carried out might be to take a picture of the finished product and put it onto the lifestyle board to see whether it looks out of place.

A lifestyle board is not an accurate reflection of any one person's life. Instead it is a very idealistic representation of the life the person may wish for. It should show the happy aspects of life with pictures full of the joys of living. The stresses and strains of real life are hardly going to be useful images for the designer to reflect in the styling of any new product.

Bigger Picture

This fifth year pupil was asked to design a hand-held electronic product for a teenager. Although he targeted older teenagers who were interested in extreme sports it is clear that the image shown opposite would appeal to a wider market either side of eighteen and nineteen year olds. The finished product is a communication device and a CD player. It has been modelled in MDF.

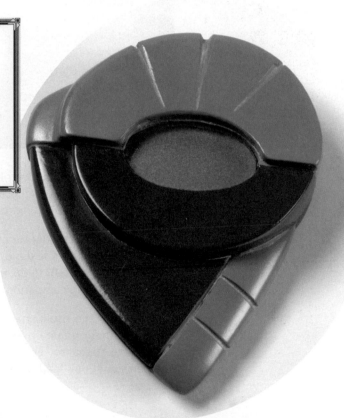

Do you think this product would look out of place in the lifestyle board opposite?

Revise as you go!

- *Describe how a lifestyle board could be used at the evaluation stage when designing a new product.*
- *What types of images are useful for a lifestyle board?*

Mood Board

A mood board is similar to a lifestyle board in that it brings together visual images from a range of sources and can act as a stimulus for design. The difference is that a mood board should create an atmosphere which reflects a chosen mood, and it can be used to help give a product a particular image. The mood of a product is the feeling or emotion aroused in us when that product is first seen.

Mood board
This shows the mood created by the body shop. This begin a care for the environment and a very natural feel

Example of a mood board.

A person's mood can be described in many ways and the images and feelings each of us experiences as a result of these moods can be different. Therefore a mood board can be a very personalised thing and may be unique to one person.

One of the main considerations must therefore be 'Who should produce the mood board?' Should it be the designer, the client, the consumer or should it be someone who has nothing at all to do with the product? There may be a case for each producing a mood board and comparing their responses.

Working with the visual images on a mood board can give a product a particular feel and an aesthetic quality that may otherwise be missing. It is not unusual for some products to appeal to certain people when they are in a particular mood or mindset. This can sometimes lead to impulse buying and consumers responding to fashions or fads.

Revise as you go!

- *Explain the difference between a mood board and a lifestyle board.*
- *Give an example of a product whose appearance is designed to reflect a mood or feeling.*

Many adjectives can be used to describe a mood. It may be useful to apply these to consumer products and then explore and experiment with the colours, shapes, lines and other aesthetic features found on the mood board.

Some moods to consider:

◆ Happy	◆ Sad	◆ Aggressive	◆ Sexy
◆ Businesslike	◆ Fun	◆ Immature	◆ Relaxed
◆ Confident	◆ Outgoing	◆ Lonely	◆ Stressed
◆ Efficient	◆ Frantic	◆ Hyperactive	◆ Cool

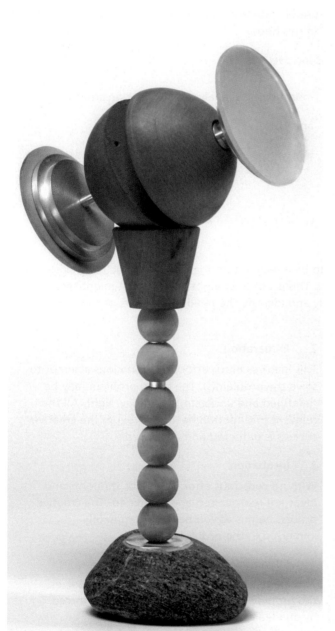

A mood board can also be a way of visual brainstorming where some of the images created by a mood are recorded and then pictures are found to illustrate them. In contrast, a lifestyle board is the result of a much more analytical process where a particular market segment is studied and visual images are then looked for and collected.

A mood board has an important role to play in establishing the styling requirements and overall image of a product. It is a good communication tool for everyone associated with the design process from the client and customer through to the design team. Mood boards should not refer to the specific product or feature of design activity.

Bigger Picture

This fifth year pupil was set the task of designing a product to be sold in the Body Shop. She decided to design a make-up mirror which could be sold as an accessory in the shop. The Body Shop has the reputation of using environmentally friendly products and promoting green issues. Clearly this has been reflected both in the mood board, on the previous page, and the finished product, left.

Lateral Thinking

Lateral thinking is a technique which encourages creativity and stimulates the imagination, often resulting in new ideas. Designers may use the process of lateral thinking to help them explore less obvious solutions to design problems.

Vertical thinking can be regarded as a linear step-by-step approach to problem solving. Solutions can also be found this way but it is a more logical and systematic approach which is less likely to produce innovative ideas.

In lateral thinking, it is not necessary to be right at every step since it is sometimes desirable to be wrong in order to organise and alter information and ideas in a new way. The provocative use of information and the challenging of accepted concepts are two of the main aspects that make lateral thinking so important to design and designing. There is no right or wrong answer, there are only better or worse solutions.

Various creative 'triggers' can be used in lateral thinking to generate alternatives. Some of these are described elsewhere in this book.

These idea generation techniques include:

- brainstorming
- mind maps
- researching information
- transfer and analogy
- morphological analysis
- analysis
- lifestyle boards
- design stories
- synthesis
- mood boards

The stages of creative thinking have been classified as follows:

1   Insight

During this first stage there has to be a recognition that a problem actually exists and a commitment is made to solving it. This is not as straightforward as it might seem. Being able to define the problem clearly and identify the needs and wants of the user can take some time.

This is a simple yet ingenious idea for a letter holder. Could the idea have come from the race of a ball bearing?

2   Preparation

This involves much effort in a conscious attempt to solve the problem(s). The given problem may be redefined and understood in a new light. All the relevant information needed to begin the creative process is gathered and organised.

3   Incubation

With no conscious effort, previous thoughts and ideas are reorganised and examined. The creative process begins as you become completely immersed in the problem.

4   Illumination

The sudden emergence of an idea which solves the problem. Your mind may have been forced by an idea generation technique to think laterally about the problem.

5   Verification

This involves a conscious development of the solution. The idea is considered and evaluated against known criteria.

Generally people will accept that design is a creative process. Good designers are creative people, but where do their ideas come from? Often we take well designed products for granted and accept the solutions they offer as being obvious. But it is through products that we can most easily identify creativity, imagination and genius yet the product rarely gives us any clue of how it came to be.

Revise as you go!

- *Write down the five stages used to describe creative thinking.*
- *List three products that you feel are unusual or different from what you expected the product to be. Discuss what you felt was different about each of them.*

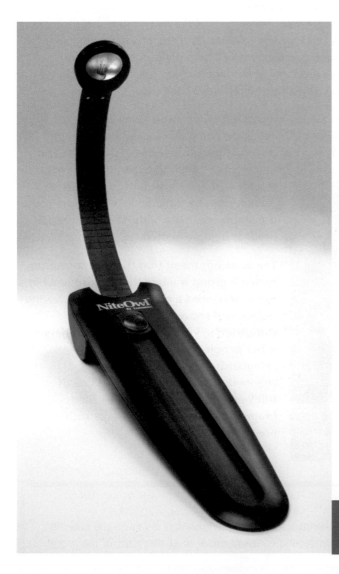

Look closely at this light. It is designed to fit between the pages at the back of a book to allow people to read in the dark. Could the idea have been inspired by a cobra?

Thought showers

Thought showering is probably the best known and most widely used technique for generating ideas. It works best as a group activity where individuals interact freely in a controlled environment. One of the advantages of this is that group members may begin to see the topic under discussion from a different point of view and so contribute new ideas. The emphasis in a thought showering session is on quantity of ideas rather than quality.

The guidelines for thought showering are straightforward.

- The problem must first be defined in simple terms to encourage a variety of potential solutions.
- At first the quantity of ideas has priority, not quality.
- Think first and evaluate later.
- No idea, however outrageous, should be disregarded by other members.
- Let free thinking develop through word association.
- Combine, expand or improve previous ideas.
- Evaluate the ideas at a later stage.
- Select and list the ideas that have merit or value.

Creating and generating ideas in this way has advantages if the group members participate and co-operate as a unit. Involvement will help members to think and express themselves; other people's ideas can encourage a chain reaction of thinking; divergent viewpoints can produce a wealth of alternative suggestions.

This 'chain-reaction thinking' can also be seen as a disadvantage. Consider the possibility that all the different lines of thinking are being channelled into a limited number of ideas. One person may suggest an idea that all the others latch on to and

immediately begin to expand and develop this idea. This means that the group's thinking can be directed in a particular route preventing the possibility of a wider range of ideas being explored.

This does not mean that thought showering within a group is a bad thing. Anyone who has experienced a group thought showering session will know how ideas can be stimulated in your own mind by listening to other people's thoughts. However safeguards must be taken to avoid channelling ideas into a limited line of thinking. There is a technique called **brainwriting** that begins to take such precautions.

Bigger Picture

Thought showering works best in a group. Free discussion is encouraged with the emphasis being on the quantity of ideas rather than the quality. Every idea is recorded by a scribe and is clearly visible to all members of the group.

Brainwriting

Brainwriting is similar to thought showering in that it actively involves a small group of people. However, they initially conduct the session in silence by writing down their own thoughts in response to the problem that has been set. These ideas are kept private so as not to influence anyone else's thinking. Each member can write their ideas on small cards or post-it stickers and keep them face down at first. Once members of the group begin to run out of ideas they can (privately) look at someone else's writing without discussing them. This should stimulate further thoughts of their own. This process continues until the group decides to discuss and share all the ideas and perhaps go on to use the thought showering process to create and generate further solutions.

Bigger Picture

Brainwriting encourages members of the group to record their own ideas and keep them private from others. Once your own ideas 'dry up' you can exchange your paper with another group member who has reached a similar stage in the hope that their ideas will stimulate a new train of thought for you.

Revise as you go!

1   *Explain the difference between thought showering and brainwriting*
1   *Write down two advantages and two disadvantages that thought showering has over brainwriting.*

Morphological Analysis

Morphological analysis is a very structured way of generating new ideas. It lends itself easily to someone working on his or her own and it encourages individual problem solving and divergent thinking. It is a visual method of seeking possible solutions and is best illustrated using diagrams with lists of subheadings which relate to a design problem.

For example, if we consider the design of a mirror, we could establish the important factors as being its market group, function, materials and theme. The next stage is to list a variety of different options for each factor, as shown below:

Market Group	Function	Materials	Theme
			pop music
5–10 years old		natural timber	Japanese
11–15 years old		aluminium	sporting
16–21 years old		MDF	environmental
22–30 years old		fabric	wildlife
31–45 years old	decoration	wood/metal	tribal
46–60 years old	promotion		cartoon
60+ years old	storage		post-modern
	display		
	make-up		
	atmosphere		
	portable		

By moving each of these lists up and down, it is possible to create 1960 (7 x 7 x 5 x 8) different word combinations. Each one can give a different idea for a new product.

The group of words highlighted in the illustration might suggest the following:

Design a mirror made mainly from wood and metal for a target market group of between 31 and 45 years old. Its main function would be decoration. Visually, it should reflect some form of tribal art.

It is clear that this type of word association is a form of paper computer, which can put together random groups of words to create a visual image of a possible product. It may be worth working with each group of words a little longer to try to generate less obvious possibilities.

Design a hand-held mirror for females younger than 31 years old. The mirror should be decorated with images associated with tribal art and made from traditional wood and metal materials.

Design a hall mirror for a modern flat. The mirror should clearly display the word 'Tribal' which is the brand name for a new up-market design company. The mirror should be decorated with non-ferrous metals and homegrown timbers. It should appeal to a wide range of people but in particular to career-oriented people in the 31–45 age bracket who are high earners.

Clearly the three design briefs have different types of products in mind, yet they have been written using the same four words from the original lists. Eventually it becomes harder to generate anything new. At that stage a different group of words can be chosen and the process allowed to continue.

A group of designers could undertake this process individually before openly discussing the **market potential** of each design brief. This is a form a **brainwriting** which can be followed up with a meeting with the whole design team to discuss further the ideas that have the most potential, before deciding which product if any to pursue.

Revise as you go!

- *Describe the method of generating design ideas through morphological analysis.*
- *What features of this process make it particularly suited to someone working on their own?*

Design Stories

Most people would agree that writing a design specification is the best way to clearly define a design problem. However, the process of writing the specification can be restrictive and can lead to predictable solutions. There appear to be very few creative methods that can be used to assist with understanding design problems and writing design specifications. Common approaches include market surveys, checklists, data collection, spider diagrams and word trees. The result will often be a collection of facts and demands which the product must meet.

Various techniques can be used at the outset of a design exercise to encourage designers to analyse problems by using their imagination and creative skills. One of these techniques involves writing 'design stories'.

During the early stages of a design project, try writing stories about the problem. The stories may be written from a variety of perspectives. Consider the following as a basis for writing a story:

- Imagine that you are the product. What would life be like?
- Imagine what life would be like without the product.
- Imagine that you are in a shop trying to sell the product to someone. How would you persuade the customer to buy this product?
- Imagine that you are trying to explain how to use the product to someone who has never seen it before.

For example, second year design students at Bournemouth University were given a design brief to design a single-use disposable tracheotomy knife for use by paramedics. The following design story was written:

'Joe is a paramedic. He's currently attending a multiple car incident on an isolated stretch of dual carriageway. One of the cars is on its side in a ditch, which is partially full of water. The passenger and driver are both unconscious and failure to wear a seatbelt has resulted in serious facial injury to the passenger who appears to be breathing badly. It is dark and light drizzle is hindering operations. There is a smell of petrol in the air, the vehicle lights are still working and the wreck is creaking ominously. Joe's task is to perform an emergency tracheotomy, by torchlight, while leaning through a smashed window.'

The story ensured that consideration was given to visual, environmental and ergonomic issues. Specific areas of research that the story inspired were: investigation of luminous polymers; consideration of the use of the knife in one hand at arm's length; grip and surface texture.

This approach ensures that open-mindedness and creativity are integral to the writing of the design specification and that the evolution of the specification plays a full part in the design process.

However it can be a useful exercise to write a design story even with a less ambitious product. Consider the following design story, which was written by a young pupil who decided to imagine what it would be like to be an eggcup for a day.

Revise as you go!
- *Explain briefly how writing a design story can help you write a specification.*
- *Explain how writing a design story from more than one person's point of view is useful.*

Hiya my name is Stan and I'm bored. All I do is stand about in this cupboard all day. I'm probably not that important. I get pushed to the side by the plates and bowls who seem to get used two or sometimes three times a day and people forget about me. There's not much space in here. Now and again I get taken out in the morning and thumped down on a table. Soon after a hot hard thing gets put inside my head and I've got to hold it while someone smashes it with a spoon or cracks it open with a knife. All this gooey stuff begins to run all over me as the inside of the hard thing is eaten. What an event that is. I'm held, squeezed, picked up and pushed around the table then left abandoned by the sink. It feels awful as the gooey stuff begins to harden and stick to me. I feel dirty and need a wash. Eventually I'm thrown in hot water and washed. People are very rough with me but I worry most when I'm rubbed dry. I always worry then in case I break. Eventually I'm put back in here in the dark and left all alone.

This story was used to help her write the specification for an eggcup which she later designed. The specification includes:

- The product needs to be small and robust.
- The product should be lively and interesting to look at.
- It must be able to hold a hot egg safely and securely.
- It should be easily cleaned.
- It should not have any dirt traps where food can get trapped.

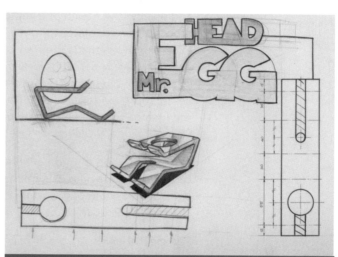

The proposed solution meets some of the criteria in the specification better than others. Can you improve this idea?

Some of the information above has been adapted from a paper presented by Nik Hills, senior lecturer in the Department of Product Design at Bournemouth University, at a seminar in Brunel University in 1997.

Bigger Picture

'Cico' eggcup with salt castor and spoon designed by Stefano Giovannoni in 2000.
It was injection moulded in thermoplastic resin. This product is unlikely to be hidden away at the back of a cupboard. It is more likely to be displayed on the breakfast bar or on a shelf in the kitchen.

Technology Transfer

New products, new ideas and inventions are often the result of a process called **associative thinking**. This means that a designer will make an association with a technology, manufacturing process or material in one area or field of design and use it to provide a new idea or solution in another. There are many examples, such as:

■ laser technology, which was developed for space and defence programmes, is now used in domestic CD systems

■ the principles of the mechanism behind ski bindings are now used in racing cycle shoes and pedals

■ the technology of an industrial cyclone separator is now used by James Dyson in his vacuum cleaners.

These examples show how a technology or idea which already exists can be transferred and used in the design of a completely new product. However it is unlikely that this process can take place without some further development or modification work. For example, Dyson made thousands of small models of the cone in the cyclone separator over a two-year period before he had a vacuum cleaner that functioned to his satisfaction. These models were hand made and tested in his own workshops before being approved for final production. This process of testing, adapting and integrating the idea or concept into a new product to make it functional, marketable and safe is one of the many challenges faced by the product designer.

Another method of using existing technology to create new products is through **combination**. Obvious examples include combined video and television sets, hi-fi systems and 'all-in-one' portable electric hand tools. A low-tech example would be an electrician's screwdriver which has a wire stripper included in the handle.

The electrician's screwdriver may seem an obvious product to have but why did no one think of it before? Being able to define problems and identify needs and market opportunities is something the designer must be able to do. Clearly an electrician will use both a screwdriver and a wire stripper for many things. He will have to carry tools and will obviously use his hands a lot while moving around, so laying tools down or misplacing them will be a common occurrence. Combining the two tools into one is an obvious solution.

Nature provides us with its own forms of technology which in a similar way can be used as the inspiration for new products. We've copied nature in many ways to help improve our lives. Consider the following examples.

■ The way in which cats' eyes reflect light is used to provide a method of marking the centre of roads.

■ Velcro was developed using principles found in goose-grass.

■ The ball and socket joint in your shoulder is copied in a variety of machines.

■ There are many examples of plants and animals providing the inspiration for the structures found in buildings and bridges.

Revise as you go!
● *Explain what is meant by the term 'Technology Transfer'.*
● *Give three examples of different product types that use the same technology.*

To take advantage of a good idea you must first understand how it works. It can take some of our most advanced technology just to work out how a plant or animal does what it does. Today in our high-tech existence much of our present technology has been inspired by nature. It would seem common sense to assume that there is still much more to learn.

Bigger Picture

In 1934 Percy Shaw invented the cat's eye which is used today to mark the centre of the road at night. It uses a material which simulates the reflective qualities of a real cat's eye to return light back towards its source.

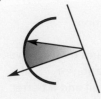

Case Study

James Dyson originally got his idea for the upright vacuum cleaner from an industrial cyclone separator. Go to **www.dyson.co.uk/** to find out how this technology makes the vacuum cleaner work. Find two other products he has designed and add them to your file.

Mind Maps

Speech and print are two of our main means of communication. Historically, it was assumed that the mind worked in a linear and list-like manner. Note-taking, for example, is usually in the form of sentences or vertical lists and there is a long-standing acceptance of this methodology. The complex process of selecting, sorting and categorising information quickly and efficiently is an important skill which can be improved by the use of 'mind mapping'.

The advantage of a mind map is that the information is 'slotted in' easily, eliminating the need to alter or rewrite. Networks of ideas and words are interlinked and added to as they are analysed, coded and criticised naturally during the process.

The following example is based on a clock project:

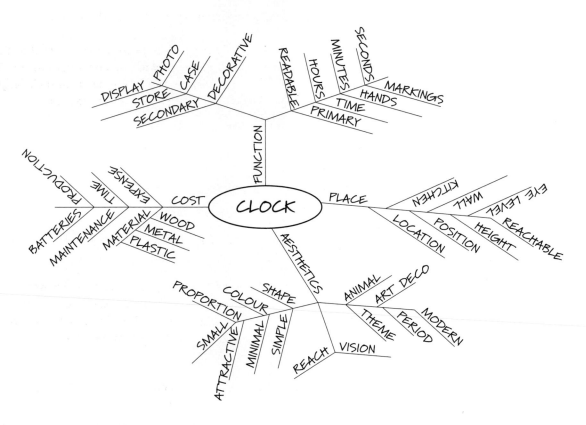

Starting from the centre, jot down ideas branching out from the main theme. This creates a pattern which is easy to remember. It also helps to link key concepts, enabling new connections to be made more readily. Then **select**, **sort** and **categorise**.

- Print in block capitals for immediate, comprehensive feedback.
- Print on lines to ensure a basic structure.
- Use one word per line.
- Be as rapid as possible without worrying about order or organisation.

Revise as you go!
- *Describe how to produce a mind map.*
- *What is the purpose of producing a mind map?*

The production of a mind map involves critical analysis, integration of information, easier recall and a better overall understanding.

Research and Development

Companies are finding it increasingly difficult to maintain growth, meet sales targets and make profits. This is due to rapid changes in fashion trends, technological developments and fierce competition from rival products. Companies can no longer depend on their existing product ranges, however successful they might be, to serve their future needs. Successful companies realise that only through active programmes of research and development (R&D) can they survive in today's competitive marketplace.

Research and development may include:

- looking for ways to make improvements to existing products
- developing new products
- extending the available range (number of models) of an existing product.

R&D departments are very expensive and ultimately can give no guarantees that their new ideas won't fail. R&D teams must therefore be very focused on what they do. They must examine market trends carefully and anticipate the future needs of their target market groups. In some ways, this is like crystal ball-gazing. Other areas for investigation may include:

- introducing new, cost-effective methods of production
- improving material specifications
- improving market research techniques
- foresighting and exploring smart materials.

These are all very time-consuming and expensive activities, so companies must consider carefully how much to invest in R&D.

New ideas and concepts need to be developed into physical products. This step requires a huge jump in investment by companies. However, this is necessary if proper testing and evaluation is to be carried out in order to decide whether the idea can be turned into a functional, commercial product. These tests could take the following forms:

- laboratory (controlled conditions) experiments or tests
- field trials, where products are tested in normal conditions of use by members of the target market group
- simulations, which could be mock-ups of real situations, carried out in controlled conditions, or computer simulations where 'virtual' situations are created.

Revise as you go!
- *List four areas a research and development team may investigate to design a new product or improve an existing one.*
- *Explain what is meant by simulation and describe how it can differ from testing.*

Communicating Ideas

Design ideas can be communicated in many different ways. Often the methods chosen will depend on which stage the design work is at and to whom the idea is being communicated. The most common method of communicating ideas is through drawings and sketches. These can be used to communicate to clients, end users, manufacturers, retailers and other designers or experts, to name but a few.

Designers will also very often sketch to communicate to themselves. Sketching ideas on paper helps them to visualise products more fully and examine problem areas better. It also frees up their minds, allowing them to develop ideas further. Written notes, comments and observations are also important methods of recording.

Some methods of communicating ideas are considered below:

- **Quick freehand sketches**   Useful for generating ideas quickly to show others or to help develop ideas that are in designers' minds.

- **Exploded drawings**   Good for showing how parts join together.

- **3-dimensional drawings**   Excellent for communicating ideas to clients and 'non-experts'.

- **Presentation drawings**   Used to communicate design proposals and finished solutions to everyone involved in a project. These include clients, consumers and retailers.

- **Scale drawings**   Used to make scale models or communicate information to manufacturers.

- **Working drawings**   Necessary for all aspects of product manufacture.

- **Computer drawings**   Most drawings of products nearing the final stage of design are now produced on computer. This enables them to be changed and updated easily and, when complete, drawings can be linked to a Computer Integrated Manufacturing system.

- **Computer simulations**   Ideal for testing and demonstrating how products will react in real life.

- **World Wide Web**   Enables information to be communicated to potential customers all over the world.

- **Scale models**   Often the first 3-dimensional representations of ideas.

- **Prototypes**   Should provide exact replicas of the proposed products and enable proper evaluations and tests to be carried out.

- **Test pieces**   Often used during development stages to test a specific aspect of any proposed solution. May involve making only a small part of a product and testing it to destruction.

- **Written reports**   Often used to communicate more technical information such as specifications, test results or evaluation studies.

A block model is a good way to show the idea to clients and possible consumers. It allows them to see it in 3D and check things like ergonomics for the first time.

Consider the types of communication used by this fifth year pupil who was set the task of designing a product for a seven-year-old that combines a limited function mobile phone and an electronic cyber pet.

For more information please refer to the section on Model-making on pages 48–9.

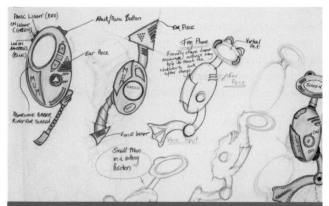

Quick pencil sketches are the easiest way to record first thoughts. They are a good way to communicate to yourself and to others in the early stages of your design work.

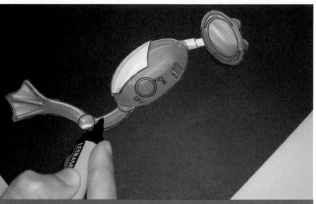

A fully rendered marker drawing is an ideal way to communicate proposed solutions to clients and others.

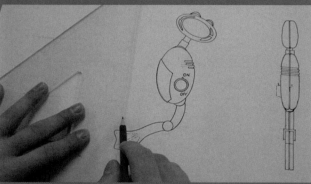

An accurate and detailed orthographic drawing is essential for model makers and manufacturers. This can also be done on computer.

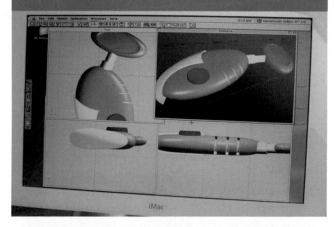

Prototypes can be tested by the intended user group before the product is released for sale.

Bigger Picture

Getting the information about the proposed product into the computer is important.

A 3-D computer model is a good way to visualise the product and make major and minor changes at no cost. The information can be stored in a .STL file and exported to a rapid prototyping facility and eventually onto full production.

Revise as you go!

- List five different types of drawing that could be used to communicate design ideas.
- What advantages does a fully crafted block model have over a presentation drawing when presenting the idea to a client?
- What advantages does pencil sketching provide over other methods of communication in the early stages of designing?

Analysis

Analysing a design problem or any suggested solution to that problem requires a close examination of what is being proposed. It involves dissecting the information into smaller, more manageable parts.

To be able to analyse a design, it is necessary to identify the needs of the user and the criteria the product must meet. This can be done by referring to the original specification and by discussing the proposal with established experts such as manufacturers, marketing people and engineers. These are focused tasks which should lead to a greater understanding of any proposal and familiarisation with how it works.

Part of the key to success is knowing the right questions to ask. Questioning is the most reliable way of stimulating the imagination. A good guide is to use questions beginning who, what, where, why, when and how. You should be able to ask many questions for each of these words. Questioning helps us to analyse by finding new relationships, applications and arrangements.

Analysing the factors which influence a design can be carried out by brainstorming headings onto a diagram and then examining each in turn:

- safety
- manufacture
- cost
- ergonomics
- market
- user
- maintenance.

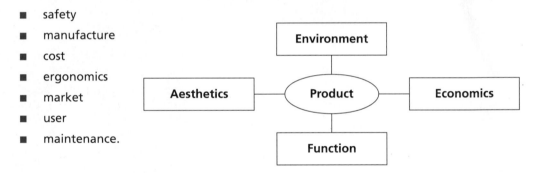

You should be able to add to this list, depending on the nature of the design problem, and then group them for further examination under the four headings shown in the diagram.

A good analysis will:

- have a methodical questioning approach
- make comparisons
- provide sufficient data to explain the product.

Research

An effective analysis identifies all the areas that need to be researched in detail. The resulting information should give more insight into various problems that could be encountered during the design process.

Designing is a creative process and it is important to explore as wide a range of ideas as possible in the time available. This requires **divergent thinking** skills especially in the early stages when the quantity of ideas is probably more important than the quality. There are many creative-thinking techniques to encourage divergent thinking and these are explored elsewhere in this book.

However there will come a time when this creative work will stop and a proper analysis needs to be made of the range of ideas that have emerged. There are many routes that can be followed towards producing a final solution but regardless of which one is taken there will always come a time when all the proposed solutions will need to be evaluated against a specification and then compared with each other. There will be strengths and weaknesses with each idea and these can be analysed systematically against every point in the specification.

An example of a pupil's work is shown below. This pupil has been very methodical in setting out each point in the specification and mapping it against each proposed idea in a matrix format. He has even taken the trouble to paste reduced photocopies of each idea onto the matrix. Although time consuming, it allowed him to get almost everything onto one sheet of paper. Good points from each idea are indicated and then all of them were pulled together to begin development work towards a final solution. The process of synthesis has begun.

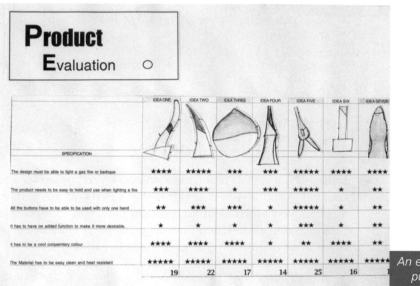

An extract from a pupil's folio.

Bigger Picture

This pupil has been very methodical in his approach to analysing the range of proposals for a product. Whichever method is chosen it is important to refer closely to the specification and record good and bad points for each idea.

Revise as you go!

- *A designer has produced a range of different design ideas. Explain how both analysis and synthesis can be used at this stage.*

- *What type of work will be undertaken during the analysis of a range of proposed solutions?*

Synthesis

Synthesis is the process of combining separate parts or elements. This can be a complicated activity and so a logical, pre-planned and systematic approach is advisable.

Synthesising provides a link between producing ideas, making decisions as to whether they are feasible or not, and producing a desirable end product. Combining and linking a collection of data, abstract thoughts, reasoning and ideas into an acceptable design solution can be aided by the use of some helpful processes and principles that help to 'tie' things together.

One of the most obvious principles of design is to make good-looking products. Simplicity of use, ease of understanding, good manufacture, correct functioning and economy of production are all equally important. When designing within limits, applying these principles gives us the opportunity to work towards a creative solution and to produce an acceptable and perhaps successful design.

A good synthesis will give due regard to the following:

- aesthetics
- ease of use
- maintenance
- function
- economics
- simplicity
- build quality

Synthesis is a part of problem solving which can be usefully compared to the art of cooking. A recipe will require that the ingredients are gathered and prepared, mixed in a certain way and cooked for a certain time. The correct ingredients, mix, heat and timing produce a delicious final dish. The same ingredients treated differently may well result in an unappetising or even inedible end result.

Solving design problems requires the best ideas to be brought together from all other proposals and developed towards one solution. This requires convergent thinking, a skill that is very analytical in nature and requires good evaluation and decision-making strategies. Usually where there is a range of good ideas one will emerge as being the best or as being the preferred choice. However it is also likely that at least some of the other ideas will have something to contribute as well.

Consider the diagram on the next page which illustrates the concept of synthesis used in the design of a desk phone for an office.

Revise as you go!
- *Explain the difference between analysis and synthesis.*
- *Describe what convergent thinking means.*

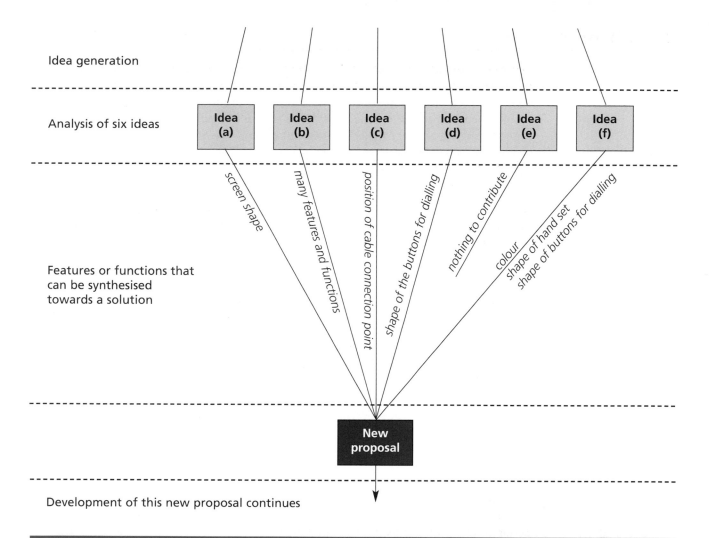

Idea generation

Analysis of six ideas

| Idea (a) | Idea (b) | Idea (c) | Idea (d) | Idea (e) | Idea (f) |

Features or functions that can be synthesised towards a solution

screen shape

many features and functions

position of cable connection point

shape of the buttons for dialling

nothing to contribute

colour

shape of hand set

shape of buttons for dialling

New proposal

Development of this new proposal continues

Synthesising ideas to create the best design solution.

Six initial ideas were presented in response to the design brief and specification. After analysing these six proposals and evaluating them against the specification idea (b) proved to be best suited for further development. However four of the other five ideas had some feature or function that was worth adding or was seen as an improvement to the main idea. Clearly idea (e) had nothing to contribute. All of these ideas were included into one developed idea, which then underwent a series of further changes and developments through 2-D and 3-D modelling before being presented as a final solution.

From the diagram it should also be clear that three proposals, including idea (b), have dialling buttons which are an attractive shape. At some stage further down the process of development one idea will begin to dominate.

Product Testing

Designers are faced with the challenge of developing new ideas into products that consumers want to buy. They also have to respond to consumer demands for new, updated models of existing products. Testing these products is a vital part of design development, especially if the designer is to ensure that consumer needs and expectations are met, consumer safety is not compromised and there is enough demand to make new products commercially viable. These tests can be carried out in a number of ways but basically there are four methods of gathering useful information:

- end-user trials
- user research
- concept testing
- expert appraisal.

End-user Trials

These require end-users (or people pretending to be end-users) to actually use products. Such experiments should include the sorts of activities that might be undertaken immediately before and after the products have been used. End-user trials can generate a number of improvements and changes that designers and manufacturers might not otherwise consider.

User Research

This may involve watching experienced and inexperienced users. They should be observed closely so that improvements and further developments to the product may be identified. Such observation can be followed up with questionnaires and discussion on how users feel about the product.

Concept Testing

This requires a new product to be tested on small groups of consumers who are part of that product's target market group. This may not always require a prototype of the product. Models, pictures or even just a description of the proposed product may be enough to establish if the idea has market potential. If a representative cross-section of the target market group is used for these tests, then an estimate of the total sales could be made. Suppose that 15% said that they would definitely buy the product. Then the company could use this figure and the market size to estimate potential sales. This has obvious advantages for deciding whether the product is likely to be profitable and for planning production.

Revise as you go!
- *Define the term 'end-user'.*
- *Describe how concept testing could be carried out.*

Expert Appraisal

This relies on the knowledge of recognised experts in the areas being tested. For example, an electronic engineer, an ergonomist and a materials expert would all be able to report on different aspects of a new microwave oven.

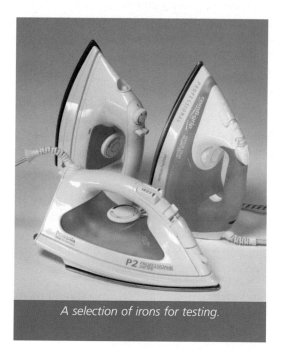

A selection of irons for testing.

Pupils testing a steam iron.

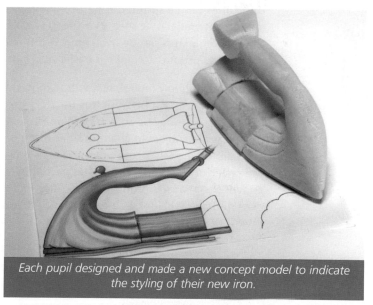

Each pupil designed and made a new concept model to indicate the styling of their new iron.

Bigger Picture

These pupils are pretending to be end users. They were each provided with a steam iron to borrow and use for a week. During this time they recorded their own views and those of the person who does the ironing at home. The next step was to demonstrate using the iron to the class and explain its good and bad points. The findings of the group were recorded and a questionnaire developed to establish the views of a much wider group. The results were collected and a new specification was written listing possible features for the new iron.

Model-making

Model-making is a necessary part of design work. It should be seen as an extension to the decision-making that all designers are involved in throughout the process.

Sketching and drawing are the most common ways of starting to design. They are quick and can be an easy way of communicating ideas to others. In the early stages of designing, a drawing will give a clear idea of aesthetic qualities such as shape, form, colour and style. It may also indicate how a product will work and provide enough information to generate a discussion on how it may be manufactured. This can be referred to as 2-dimensional modelling. However, a drawing will provide no information on the performance of a product. Even basic product requirements such as stability, strength, flexibility, ergonomics and safety need to be tested on models and prototypes. As a result of these tests, alterations may have to be made to the initial idea. These have to be recorded, along with the reasons for the changes. Further models and prototypes can then be made and tested again.

Models also provide designers with opportunities to look at their designs in three dimensions for the first time. Designers can walk around, look through and examine how natural light enhances a modelled product's edges, curves and overall form. In many ways modelling is like a sculptor working on an art form, making aesthetic decisions as and when required.

Prototypes are different from models in that they should be exact replicas of the finished commercially produced product. This is useful in many ways, especially as it allows the designer the chance to experience all the manufacturing stages. Design for manufacture is a vital part of the process of design and previously unforeseen difficulties can be sorted out before going to full production. In this respect, models and prototypes can be seen as a cheap way of avoiding mistakes. Difficulties in making jigs and templates can be overcome at this early stage, even if this means redesigning a part of the product to make it easier and more economical to manufacture.

Before making any model, many drawings, sketches and templates have to be made. These are important because it is through them that the model maker will experience how difficult it may be to work accurately to a design proposal. However, these drawings are subject to change. New, more precise drawings will have to be produced once all the models, prototypes and tests have been completed. These drawings will be the result of this work and will be passed over to the manufacturing company in the knowledge that the product can be mass manufactured accurately, will perform as expected and will look and feel the way the designer has visualised.

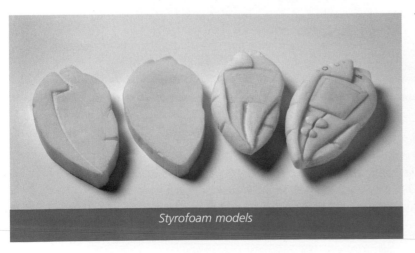

Styrofoam models

This fifth year pupil used modelling to help her make ergonomic, aesthetic and manufacturing decisions about her design for a route finder/mobile phone. Early models were quick to produce and left in an unfinished state as they were used only to establish the position of standard components such as screens, buttons and dials. Later models were styled more to show aesthetic features and forms. The early presentation drawing shown was produced prior to making the block model. This provided her with a clear understanding and an accurate representation of the proposal. Further decisions about the design were made during the block modelling stage, which resulted in updates to the final production drawings.

Bigger Picture

Modelling in materials that can be worked easily is a quick method of exploring the 3-dimensional qualities of an idea. The styrofoam used here is a fine celled expanded polystyrene. It can be glued with PVA adhesive and painted with water-soluble paints. These 'sketch models' were left unfinished as they had served their purpose allowing the pupil to progress to the next stage.

High level sketching and drawing skills enable everyone to visualise for the first time what is being proposed. This drawing could be the focus of discussions with manufacturers, clients and other designers. The feedback from these people would be used to take the idea to the next stage.

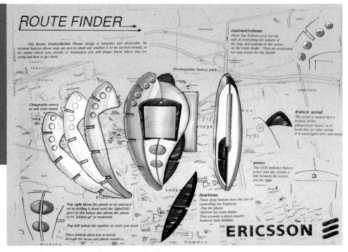

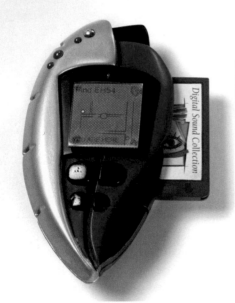

The block model is much more accurate and is finished to look exactly like the final product. All external details are visible and all surfaces give a true representation of the proposed finished product.

Revise as you go!

- *Write down three different types of model that could be used by a designer when developing a new product. Discuss the advantages of each of these models.*

- *Describe where and why a designer would use styrofoam to model in preference to a solid material.*

Case Study

'Benchmark' is one of the UK's leading specialists in industrial model making and prototype development. Visit their website at **www.benchmark.u-net.com** Find out about their approach to model making and view some of their most recent models. Write down the different types of modelling services they provide and add this to your file.

Evaluation

Evaluation is a necessary and vital part of the design process. It should be something that occurs naturally throughout the process, with continual reference being made to the specification. Evaluation should not be regarded as something that is only carried out once the product is made.

We evaluate commercial products every day both consciously and subconsciously. In most cases we make comparisons, known as 'benchmarking', with other similar product types and form value judgements based on previous experiences and personal preferences. However, designers need to be more objective than consumers and perhaps more scientific in their approach. The evaluation of any product requires a detailed and individual set of criteria. These criteria should include functions and features that are specific to that particular product. This makes it impossible to produce one complete checklist that can be used to evaluate completely different product types such as mobile phones and domestic kettles. However, it is possible to consider both of these product types under more general criteria.

General Evaluation Criteria

The following questions should be treated as general headings which should lead to a more specific line of questioning for the product being evaluated.

- Is it suited to its purpose?
- Is it easy to use?
- Is it good-looking?
- Is it simple to maintain?
- Is it well made?
- Is it safe?
- Is it good value for money?
- How does it affect the environment?

Specific Evaluation Criteria

Remember that the above list is only a guide. More detailed questions need to be asked about the product being evaluated. For example, if a kettle is being evaluated then under the heading 'Is it easy to use?' more specific questions need to be asked. These in turn may lead to experiments or tests being carried out. Examples include:

- Does it pour easily?
- Can the water level be checked easily?
- Is it easy to fill?
- Is it easy to lift?

It is obvious that different questions and tests would apply to the mobile phone if it were being evaluated under the same heading.

It is very difficult to evaluate a product without comparing it to something else. For instance in the evaluation of a hairdryer one of the first tests that can be done is to assess its weight. When asked to comment on this people usually say that it is either light or heavy. However this judgement can only be made using personal experience of the weight of other hairdryers. A scientific approach would be to weigh each hairdryer and record the result.

A more natural approach to evaluating products is to carry out a comparative study for several similar product types. A scoring system can be used to grade each one of the specific criteria for each product. To do this fairly and efficiently the following guidelines should be observed.

- Both quantitative (measurable) and qualitative (qualities assessed by judgement) can be used.
- The specific criteria to be used for evaluation should be clear before starting.
- The same tests should be carried out for each product.
- The tests should be carried out in identical conditions for each product.
- The same scoring system should apply to each criterion for each product.

Consider applying a factor to the overall score for each criterion depending on its perceived importance. For example heat output of a hairdryer could be deemed 3 times more important than its appearance. Therefore the score given for this would be multiplied by 3.

Which? *magazines report regularly on consumer products like kettles, steam irons and cordless kettles.*

The testing and evaluation of consumer products is a specialist field where researchers have access to an array of equipment, services and technical experts. Generally as far as testing and evaluation are concerned there is a recognisable basic format and procedure which can be followed.

Revise as you go!

- *Write down five considerations, which are important in the design of a domestic iron.*
- *Explain what is meant by a comparative study.*
- *Describe the conditions under which a comparative study should be carried out.*

SECTION 2
Principles

Section 2: Principles

Defining the Market

The original meaning of the term 'market' is a place where buyers and sellers gather to exchange goods. Many towns had market squares where sellers brought their goods for people to buy. Today most of the buying and selling of goods is done in shopping centres and high streets.

A market can be described as the set of potential buyers of a product or service. The size of the market will depend on the number of buyers of a particular product. Potential buyers for a product will have three things in common: interest, income and access.

Interest, Income and Access

Mountain bike for teenage boys fourteen or above.

Consider the market for mountain bikes. We must first estimate the number of people who have an interest in owning a mountain bike. The potential market is the number of people who have some level of interest in mountain bikes.

This interest alone is not enough to accurately define the total market for a mountain bike. Any potential consumer must also have enough income to afford the bike. Therefore the size of the market depends on both income and interest.

The market size can be reduced further, for example, if the company who manufactures the bike does not distribute to certain areas or if there is no appropriate retail outlet in those areas. Therefore, the available market can be defined as those consumers who have interest in the bike and have the income and access to buy it.

Bigger Picture

Think about how the above considerations relate to the other sections in this book and in your course. Refer to Section 2: Consumer Expectations, Economic Considerations and Aesthetic Considerations and think about the consequences that Interest, Income and Access will have on developing design proposals.

Characteristics of the Market

It may also be that the company may wish to discourage part of the available market from using the bike. In this case the company may not wish to sell the bike to children under the age of thirteen or to those who may find this mountain bike too big. Those children who are fourteen years or above and are physically mature enough are known as the **qualified available market**.

As soon as the qualified available market has been defined, the company can then decide which part of that group it wishes to target. It may, of course, decide to target the whole group and not just a segment of it. Whichever group it decides to pursue is then referred to as the **served market**.

There may well be people within this served market who already own the product. This is known as the **penetrated market**.

The diagram illustrates these concepts using hypothetical figures.

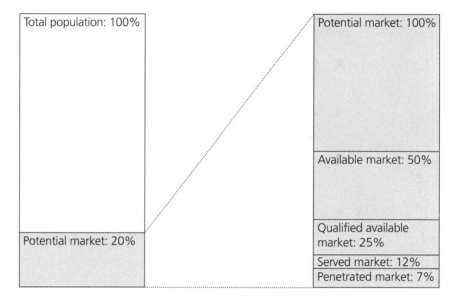

Using these figures we can work out that the mountain bike is aimed at 5% of the total population. This is the difference between the served market and the penetrated market.

Revise as you go!

- *Explain the difference between the potential market and the available market.*
- *Why is it necessary for a designer to know exactly who a product is being designed for?*
- *Give four examples of how effective market research would highlight aspects such as interest, income and access.*

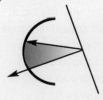

Case Study

Designing products for a specified market is something designers do regularly. Browse through the products, furniture and jewellery shown at **www.designnation.co.uk** paying particular attention to who the product is designed for. Choose six of your favourite designs and add them to your file noting alongside who they are for and what materials they are made from.

Market Segments

Few products, if any, can be said to compete in a global or mass market. Most companies now practise **target marketing** which directs products at one or more groups of consumers who share common needs and wants. Market segmentation will assist with this because it divides the market into distinct groups of buyers with different needs who might require separate products or marketing mixes.

Market segments can be thought of as groups of people who have something in common that will affect their choice of product. There are many ways to define a particular market group, using a variety of factors, but generally they can be grouped into four major categories:

- **Geographic**

  such as countries, regions, cities

- **Demographic**

  such as age, sex, income, education, race

- **Psychographic**

  such as personality, lifestyle, social class

- **Behaviouristic**

  such as purchase frequency, usage, benefits sought, brand loyalty.

Each of these **market segments** can be broken down further and products can be targeted at a much narrower group of people. For example, if we look at age and divide the population into six segments, it may look something like this:

5–10 years	This age group could be classified as **fun** years.
11–17 years	These are often **fashion**-driven years.
18–25 years	Most people become **independent**.
26–35 years	Many people are motivated by their **career**.
36–55 years	Often **family** becomes the major priority.
56+ years	This is a time when more **choice** is available.

These age bandings can be redefined in any way that the designer sees fit. It is also useful to note that because a product is targeted at one specific age group it will not stop someone from another group liking it. This is especially true for the age bandings at either side.

Small firms often find it easier to divide the population into much smaller segments and the six age bands above can be divided further by using other demographic or even behaviouristic factors to restrict the target market. This strategy of identifying a specialist segment is called **niche marketing**. A niche is a small group of consumers that can be defined in specific terms. The group will normally have very distinctive characteristics which may involve some area of their lifestyle, hobbies or interests. Consider teenagers attending high school. Generally people in this age group are motivated by style and appearance and are very image conscious. They may find themselves following clothing trends or buying products that allow them to be easily identified as part of that group. Examples include grunge, skateboarders and Goths.

Market segmentation requires the market to be divided into distinct groups of potential consumers. These groups may find certain products inappropriate or may need a different type of the same product. Consider the four cameras shown. They all take photographic images therefore can be classed as being of the same **product type**. However they are aimed at different market groups whose lifestyle demands a certain type of camera. Each camera can be said to be **fit for its purpose**.

This 35mm camera made by Fisher Price is aimed at young children. It is robust and can withstand being dropped and bumped.

This disposable camera made by Kodak is useful for teenagers at parties or nights out. Also at around £5.00 it provides a cheap last-minute option for someone who has forgotten their camera.

This mid range digital camera by Fuji is popular with many in the 18–25 age group. This or one like it may well be their first serious digital camera.

Designed by Fuji this digital camera is more expensive and heading towards the top of the mid range cameras. It would certainly appeal to consumers who are a little older with more disposable income and who are perhaps beginning to take photography a little more seriously.

Revise as you go!

- *What is meant by the term 'target market'?*
- *Describe two ways in which a market group can be selected.*
- *What is a market niche?*

The Marketing Mix

To enable a well designed product to compete successfully in a very overcrowded market place will require a good marketing strategy. Although the designer may not be directly involved in the selling, advertising or marketing of their product it is useful for them to have some understanding of what is involved and have an opportunity to contribute.

Once the market has been defined and researched and the target market group has been identified, the company is ready to begin planning the details of the marketing mix. The marketing mix consists of everything that can be done to influence the demand for the product. There are many possibilities, but these can all be grouped together under four headings known as the **four Ps: product, price, place and promotion**.

The Four Ps

Product

Anything that can be offered to the market for use to satisfy a want or a need. Often a product will be part of a range produced by the same company. This range will offer consumers choice within the same brand and will include products at the top, middle and bottom in terms of features and facilities.

Price

This is the amount charged by the company or exchanged by the consumer for a product. The company must consider the selling price carefully. It should reflect the image that they are trying to promote for the product. For example designer labels have hugely inflated price tags so as to create the impression that it is a quality product which is reliable and safe. Paying more money for a top-of-the-range product can give consumers that feel-good factor

Place

All the company's activities that make the product available to the customer. These will include selling on the internet, mail catalogue and even interactive TV. However the company must be sure that the product is being seen in the right places by their target market group.

Promotion

Any activity which will advertise the product and its benefits to potential buyers. To a certain extent this relates to technology push. Consumers need to be given information about this new product and made aware of its benefits and the advantages it holds over its competitors.

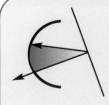

Case Study

IKEA are a Swedish based company who specialise in designing products for use in the home. Visit their website at **www.ikea.co.uk/student_info.html** to find out how they successfully use the 4 Ps of the marketing mix.

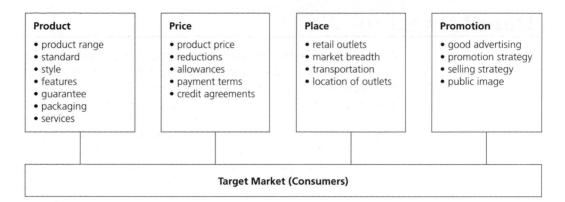

An effective marketing programme will combine all four elements into an effective strategy designed to promote the product.

Consumer Benefit

These four Ps represent the seller's view of how marketing can influence whether or not a consumer will buy a product. However we must be aware that each of these points must deliver a customer benefit and as far as the product is concerned this benefit has to evolve during the design, development and planning stages. Consider the following:

Product

The product meets the consumer's needs/wants. These needs and wants should be clearly defined at the early stages of writing the design brief.

Price

The cost to the consumer should be affordable and competitive. Market research should indicate what the consumer is willing to pay for this product and what the likely sales figures should be. This will indicate profit margins and ultimately could affect decisions made on materials to be used and methods of manufacture. In a worst case scenario it may even suggest that proceeding with an idea past the design stage will not prove economically viable.

Place

The product is accessible to the consumer to buy. The design team need to know where this new product is likely to be positioned in the market in order to establish the retail outlets it is likely to be sold in and what it will have to compete with on the shelf next to it.

Promotion

The product should appeal to the consumer. It should have a visual presence that makes a potential buyer take more than a passing interest in it.

Revise as you go!

- *Describe three of the factors that contribute to the final sale price of a product.*
- *Explain how the four Ps can influence the demand for a product.*

Needs

A human need is often described as a state of felt deprivation. There are many human needs which we have all experienced at one time or another. Some are basic, such as our need for food, water and clothing. However we have other more socially interactive needs which can be more complicated to define, such as the need to belong and to feel wanted and our need for affection. There are also private individual needs for knowledge and self expression. All of these needs are a fundamental part of the human make up and are not falsely created by design companies and market researchers. However designers have studied human behaviour and realised that if any of these needs are not satisfied, then a person may do one of two things:

- try to reduce or eliminate the need
- look for an object or a product to satisfy the need.

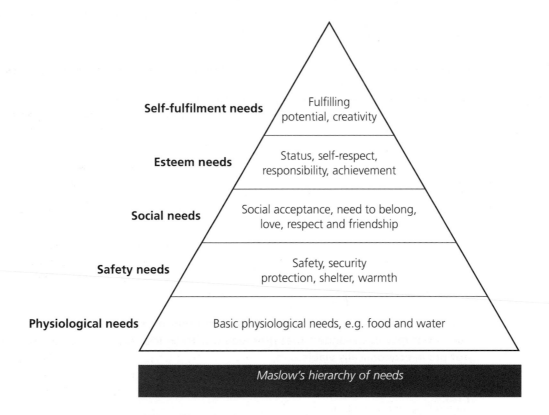

Self-fulfilment needs — Fulfilling potential, creativity

Esteem needs — Status, self-respect, responsibility, achievement

Social needs — Social acceptance, need to belong, love, respect and friendship

Safety needs — Safety, security protection, shelter, warmth

Physiological needs — Basic physiological needs, e.g. food and water

Maslow's hierarchy of needs

The American psychologist Abraham Maslow explored the reasons why some people are motivated and driven by particular needs at particular times. He concluded that human needs are arranged in a hierarchy, from the most basic level to those that are least vital to human survival. In order of importance they are:

Revise as you go!

- *Use examples of products to explain the difference between needs and wants.*
- *Give an example of two products that satisfy a human need. State clearly what the need is in each case.*

1 **physiological** needs

2 **safety** needs

3 **social** needs

4 **esteem** needs

5 **self-fulfilment** needs.

A person will try to satisfy the most important need first. When that is done, the person will then move on to try to satisfy the next most important need.

Maslow's hierarchy of needs is not true for all people in all cultures but it is often used by market researchers and designers as a general rule of thumb.

Europe today has a vibrant market economy where most of us have access to products, activities and information that will go a long way towards addressing all of our needs. Our high street and shopping centres are full of shops selling products designed to help and benefit us in some way.

Our basic needs remain the same. We still need food and water but our ability to store, prepare and consume is made more hygienic, safe and enjoyable by a whole range of kitchen products and appliances such as kettles, cookers, fridges and even basic utensils like knives and forks. Toothbrushes and electric showers are taken for granted in most homes now as are many other products that satisfy our need to live safely and healthily. We still need to boil water for a variety of reasons but the way we do it has become more sophisticated over the years.

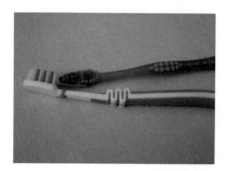

Bigger Picture

Nobody would argue that in the interests of health and hygiene we all need to brush our teeth. Toothbrush design has come a long way especially since recent developments in plastics provide materials which are both strong and flexible.

Designers recognise that generally all of our needs are catered for and that the products presently available benefit us in some way. However they will continue to develop these further, looking for ways to make new products quieter, quicker, safer, more efficient and more environmentally friendly.

People with nut allergies are constantly at risk from an anaphylactic attack if they come into contact with any nut or nut substance. This is a life-threatening condition which is present twenty-four hours a day and an attack must be treated with an injection of adrenalin. Until recently this was done by drawing the adrenalin out of a bottle into a syringe in a conventional way before injecting into the leg. Apart from being time consuming there are obvious risks associated with carrying syringes around, not to mention the problems and stress for the person having to administer the injection. The 'Epipen' is a recent development which is safe to carry and easy to use. It is a product which demonstrates how designers continue to meet people's needs by offering improved benefits over existing products.

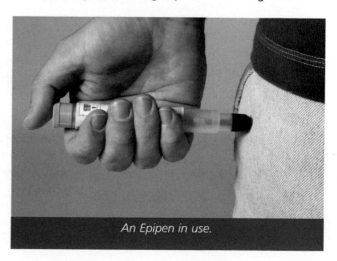

An Epipen in use.

Wants

Designers are now able to develop existing products by improving their features and functions much faster than ever before. Manufacturers can also produce things more quickly and cheaply, making new products more accessible to more people. Today we are surrounded by a choice for everything from a tin opener to a family car. New products are appearing almost daily and because of this there is huge competition between rival companies who try to make consumers **want** to buy their model in preference to another brand. Choice can be influenced by subtle and sometimes not-so-subtle marketing techniques but generally consumers will have their own reasons for wanting to buy a new product.

There can be many reasons for wanting a product. It may:

- make our lives easier
- help us to feel part of a group
- provide us with a feeling of safety
- help us to be better informed
- give us social status
- improve our health and wellbeing.

Wants are often described in terms of objects that will satisfy needs. These objects will depend on an individual's personality, their wellbeing and the culture they are living in. A good example would be to consider a group of people who all **need** to eat. Each one of them, however, may **want** to eat different things.

Products, too, can fulfil different needs. Toys provide children with an opportunity to learn, relax and interact with their peers. This is true for all children in all cultures, but the more advanced and developed the market economy in which they live, the more children seem to want to fulfil these needs with more advanced and expensive toys.

Many children living in advanced economies would find it socially unacceptable to play with the primitive toys used by children in third-world cultures. They **expect** the latest toys and the most up-to-date versions of them. Even at an early age they are becoming image-conscious, using material things to fulfil their needs for social acceptance, respect and friendship.

Peer pressure and social aspiration is not simply *there*: it is manufactured in society, by the media and marketeers creating want and expectation.

Domestic products provide further evidence of people's **want** for products which say something about themselves. This means that the products they purchase give them some kind of satisfaction through 'what they say' to them or to people in their social circles, rather than just through 'what they do'. Products have a meaning beyond their practical function.

The opportunity to make such choices is the result of living in an affluent society where the basic function of a product is taken for granted. Much of the world would be grateful for any kind of kettle to boil water, never mind a choice of cordless jug kettles in numerous styles with different features.

However, research has shown that any culture will try to differentiate between social subgroups by forms of personal display.

People have narrow, basic needs such as food, shelter and clothes to keep them warm. We have already looked at how, in different economies, they can be faced with a choice of products or services to meet these needs. Most people have limited resources and will choose products that will provide the most satisfaction for their money. If they can back this up with the ability to pay, these **wants** become **demands**.

Consumers view products as providing them with a benefit. They will choose products that give them the most benefits for their money and these need not always be functional benefits. Given their wants, resources and interests, people will **demand** products that provide them with the most benefits.

Revise as you go!

- *Give three examples of products that you feel people have bought to boost their personal image. Give reasons for your choice.*
- *Discuss how the design and the marketing of a product can make it desirable.*

Technology Push/Market Pull

There is little point designing products that nobody wants. If people do not want a particular product, then it fails. New product innovations are appearing regularly and their designers always consider them to have market potential. Many are based on new technology and many others are based on what the designer feels people need or want. We can therefore consider product development and innovation as having two main driving forces: the **push** that is the result of new developments in technology and the **pull** of consumer needs, wants and aspirations.

Technology Push

Through research, scientists, engineers and designers often discover new technology or new applications for existing technology which can be used in the development of new products. Consumers are oblivious to these products at first, many being beyond their imagination and experience. They only become aware of their existence when they appear in shops or are advertised through the media. This type of product can prove to be a huge risk for the manufacturer. Here we have a new product which uses new technology offering new benefits to the consumer. It sounds as though it cannot fail but not all such products are successful. This approach to product development is referred to as **technology push**. Examples include:

- new materials which have improved properties. 'Smart' materials which react and change when exposed to light, heat and moisture are now being used in products like sunglasses and domestic kettles.

- new methods of manufacture which can offer aesthetic, functional, economic or environmental benefits to products. Advances in the way plastic can be moulded have seen two-shot moulds and multi-cavity moulds used more frequently.

- smaller components which can lead to miniaturisation. Hand-held electronic products such as mobile phones, digital cameras and personal music players are now more powerful and offer an increasing range of functions and features.

- improved technology which makes products quicker, more powerful, more efficient and more intelligent. Laptop computers, programmable washing machines as well as a range of medical equipment that can monitor, analyse and record a variety of conditions and ailments.

Bigger Picture

Consumer demand for environmentally friendly products caused manufacturers to stop making fridges and aerosol cans that contained CFC gases.

New technology can create new markets. This may be through product evolution where the product is simply a better version of an existing one. Alternatively, it may be that a 'product type' which has not existed before is produced, so creating a completely new market niche. One of the most famous examples of this is the Sony Walkman.

Revise as you go!

- *Describe what is meant by the terms 'market pull' and 'technology push'.*
- *Name two products that you feel have been designed as a result of each of these strategies.*

Market Pull

Consumer demand (market pull) encourages products that derive from the demands of the marketplace. These demands are often identified through market research. Some examples of consumer demand are:

- more environmentally friendly products
- products that can be identified with certain fashion trends or styles
- products that include more up-to-date technology.

These consumer demands or wishes could lead to further research work being done in areas such as material technology, production, electronics and artificial intelligence. This in turn can encourage designers, engineers and scientists to develop products which in a sense are being 'pulled' into the market place by the consumer. However it is often difficult to know if a product has been driven by consumer demand or by the company having pushed these products on to us. They will be marketed in such a way as to have us believe that we need them and they are an essential part of our lives.

Bigger Picture

The Sinclair C5 was launched in 1985 and was the first electrically assisted tricycle to be mass-produced. It was very progressive in both in its technology and ergonomics and it was advertised as a 'world first' in 'personal transport powered by electricity'. It proved to be a commercial disaster and the company went into receivership after eight months having lost over £8 million. The C5 was unsafe given its low riding position and lack of crash protection. It quickly attracted a poor image and became a product that was laughed at and made fun of. It was neither a car nor a bike and ultimately paid the price for being unable to compete with either.

The Sinclair C5

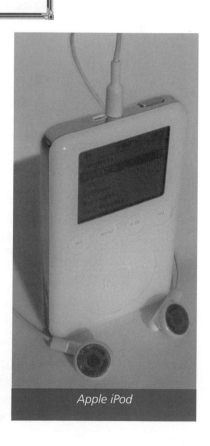
Apple iPod

Bigger Picture

MP3 players, such as the Apple iPod, were first introduced to the market in the late 1990s. They allowed users to store vast amounts of music and gave them almost instant access to it using a new form of solid state technology that had never before been used in personal music players.

Marketing or Selling

Marketing can often be confused with selling or advertising. These are the two most visible components of marketing with which we are continually bombarded through television commercials, newspaper advertisements, telephone sales and street ads. However, selling and advertising are only part of greater marketing strategies which include assessing **customer needs**, carrying out **market research**, developing products that provide superior **value** and offer the consumer **benefits**, together with **distributing**, **pricing** and **promoting** the product effectively. If a company achieves all of these and responds to consumer demands, then its products will sell very easily.

> **Revise as you go!**
> - *Describe what you think are the differences between marketing and selling.*
> - *Explain what is meant by the term a 'sellers' market'.*

Designing products that offer benefits to the consumer and marketing them well are the keys to success.

Good examples include the use of new technology by Sony when it first brought its Walkman and, later, its Discman to the market. Nintendo was swamped with orders when it offered a new games console with improved product features. The Body Shop responded to a market demand for cosmetics that were not tested on animals.

These three product examples can claim to be **innovative** and therefore the marketing effort must emphasise the **benefits** that the consumer will gain by using them.

Designers are constantly supplying companies with new ideas, of which only a handful are so successful that they eventually become household names. One reason for rejecting a product might be that it is not distinctive enough. It should provide a benefit or a feature that makes it stand out from other similar products. Very often these distinguishing features are very minor ones.

There are two types of market:

- **A Sellers' Market**

  Companies may disregard consumer wants and focus on their own production, making products that they want to make. This usually results in a lack of choice for the consumer and will normally be successful only if the company is faced with little or no competition. The most famous example of a sellers' market is Henry T Ford saying about the then new model T Ford car 'They can have any colour so long as it is black'. This showed a total disregard for consumer preferences but Ford had over 50% of the American car market through out the 1920s.

- **A Buyers' Market**

  The consumer is usually faced with a choice between similar products. There will be a variety and a range of products to choose from. This will be brought about by competition from other companies or quite often from an extensive product range produced by the same company.

'The aim of marketing is to make selling superfluous. The aim is to know and understand the customer so well that the product or service fits … and sells itself.'

Peter Drucker (management and business adviser)

The Smart car was launched in 1998 and since then it has grown in popularity due to a successful marketing campaign. Originally the car was developed as a joint venture between the German car manufacturer Mercedes Benz and the Swiss watch company Swatch.

© Martin Goddard/CORBIS

Interchangeable body panels are injection moulded in thermoplastic making them fully recyclable. All the body panels on the car can be replaced for under £500. It is possible to mix and match the colours.

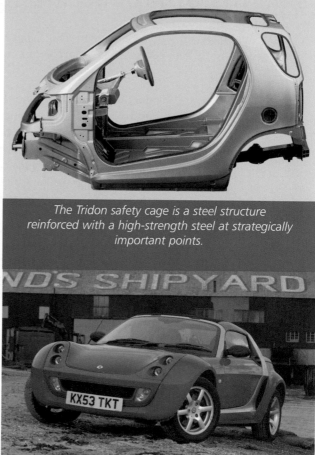

The Tridon safety cage is a steel structure reinforced with a high-strength steel at strategically important points.

The Smart car is marketed as being safe and fun to drive.

The Smart Roadster – high-strength steel at strategically important points.

Today the car has a range of models and styles with a variety of specifications. Their marketing director Philip Schiemer said, 'As our customer structure is unusually wide the greater choice of variants is a further measure to comply with the wishes of Smart drivers. Customers are different and their Smarts are also configured to their individual needs.'

The car is marketed as a kind of lifestyle accessory for those under 30 and as an economical car which is easy to park for the city executive. Its unique 'Tridon' safety cage has a universal appeal as does its fuel efficiency, which is in excess of 60 miles per gallon. For the environmentalist it gives out extremely low emissions and at the end of its life it can be returned and fully recycled. There is a full range of stylish accessories which allow customers to personalise their car from exterior colour combinations to interior fabric. Smart have worked hard at marketing what consumers once regarded as a 'curious little car'. During their advertising campaigns they asked consumers to 'Open your mind. You'll only find unusual solutions by asking unusual questions.'

Like every other product that exists in a highly competitive market place, marketing a car has replaced simply selling one. Faced with such stiff competition Henry Ford might have changed his philosophy to, 'You can have every colour as well as black.'

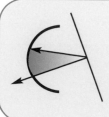

Case Study

BMW are a company who have a reputation for producing quality cars. Visit their website at **www.bmweducation.co.uk** to find out more about their marketing policy. Make your own notes about this and add them into your file.

Benefits of Product Design

'... good design starts from the premise that living is more than just a matter of existing, and that everyday things which are both effective and attractive can raise the quality of life.'

Sir Terence Conran

Product design is all around us. We live with it every day and it has now become such a necessary part of our existence that we would struggle to survive without it. However, the way in which we design products has changed over the years. The impact of new technologies and manufacturing systems has altered the way we approach designing. No longer is the appearance of a product dictated by the way it works. The aesthetics of many products are no longer determined by their mechanics thanks to new computer chip technology and miniaturisation.

Aesthetics, appearance and style have become such important parts of our lives that consumers often sacrifice quality, ease of use and value for money in their quest to remain 'in vogue'. The products we choose to surround ourselves with say something about us and indicate our values, customs and culture. Such is the scope of new materials, new technologies and advanced manufacturing systems that it is possible to design a microwave oven and a hi-fi system which look the same.

In this new century, the possibilities offered by product design promise a lot of pleasant surprises. However, product designers must take more responsibility for the products they design and the impact these will have on our lives. Unfortunately designers don't always get it right: aerosols, fridges and the motor car engine can all be cited as having a detrimental effect on the environment in some way or another. It may well be argued however that the benefits of these products outweigh any damage caused. We need designers, employers and manufacturers who have social consciences and consider the way their designs will integrate and interact with everyone and everything that they come into contact with.

Products have the ability to enhance our existence or to hinder it. Ultimately, they should be easy and enjoyable to use. They should provide benefits to everyone who comes into contact with them and, because they play such an important part in our lives, it is critical that they are well designed.

Some of the Benefits Product Design can Offer

A product can:

- improve the quality of life of the user
- give an improved performance over previous models
- provide the user with status
- minimise manufacturing costs
- create a new market or expand the existing market
- increase company profits
- use existing resources more economically
- create a new or better aesthetic.

Revise as you go!
- *Write down four ways in which a product can offer a benefit to its user.*
- *Discuss how improving the aesthetics of a product offers a benefit to the user.*

Who could deny that the telephone has improved the quality of life both at work and at home? The telephone at work is now indispensable. The mobile phone brings many benefits including greater safety and instant communication through voice and text.

Bigger Picture

In 1999 Professor Michael Wilson invented a method of purifying water after watching a sultana expand, absorbing water through its skin. His invention, Cellopore, has the potential to reap enormous benefits for people in disaster areas, giving them clean, safe water from any source. It requires no chemicals or fuel, is biodegradable and excludes 99.99% of micro-organisms, bacteria and viruses.

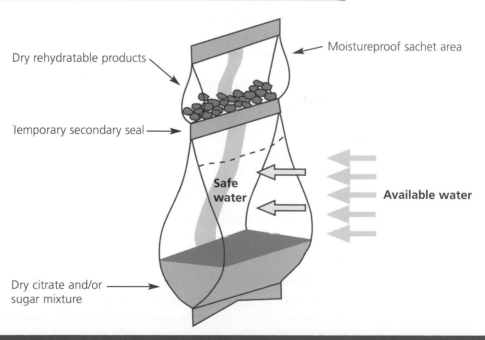

Dry rehydratable products

Moistureproof sachet area

Temporary secondary seal

Safe water

Available water

Dry citrate and/or sugar mixture

Cellopore double sachet

Product Planning

Deciding on which product is right for which market is a very important decision for a designer or company. Clearly this will be guided by market research, technological developments and market demands.

There are four options open to the designer as a basic product strategy is formulated.

		Products	
		Existing	**New**
Markets	**Existing**	Market Penetration (existing market, existing product)	Product Development (existing market, new product)
	New	Market Development (new market, existing product)	Diversification (new market, new product)

- **Market Penetration**

  This is an attempt to increase the sales of a product through activities such as advertising, promotions and special offers. Could be regarded as 'injecting new life into an old product'.

- **Product Development**

  Deciding to develop new or improved products for an existing or established market. This may simply be giving an existing product a face-lift or expanding the product range. However a decision needs to be made as to whether to remove the existing product from the market thereby removing competition from the new product or keeping it there to try to capture a bigger share of the market.

- **Market Development**

  A strategy for company growth by identifying and developing new markets and new market segments for current company products. This can be done by finding new users, new customers or foreign markets.

- **Diversification**

  This can be done by designing, developing and selling new products in new markets. This is easily the most risky of the four strategies. Diversification usually requires much market research and a comprehensive product development programme. If the finished product does not prove to be successful or popular and sales are low it will cost the company a lot of money.

Before deciding on any of these strategies a company must first examine its present product range and establish what stage they are at in the product life cycle. The closer a product gets to maturity the closer it gets to its sales beginning to decline. At this stage some form of new product development is required. Any one of the four strategies above if successful will increase sales. The decision for the company is which one will be best.

In 1972 the first Nike training shoe was introduced to the market. This was designed specifically as a racing shoe for athletes. Since then the company has grown steadily by continually developing a stream of leading-edge training shoes in what is now a very competitive market. Its shoes are still worn by athletes though this is a small part of their customer base. They primarily target the 'Youthful Market' where high performance training shoes are a fashionable and desirable product. Since 1972 Nike have used each of the four strategies successfully at one time or another. They now produce hundreds of footwear designs each year sometimes making their own or another company's obsolete. They now sell worldwide and the famous swoosh logo is recognised everywhere. Their advertising campaigns have been very successful to the point where people recognise the 'Just Do It' slogan without the word Nike appearing.

Nike are no longer just a company that manufactures training shoes. They have diversified their product range to include sunglasses, watches, MP3 players and even perfume.

Revise as you go!

- *Explain what is meant by the term 'diversification'.*
- *Why is this strategy of product planning risky for a company?*
- *How could market research help companies who are thinking of diversifying?*

Product Life Cycle

Every product will pass through a number of stages during its life. However, the length of time between a product's introduction to the marketplace and its withdrawal may vary a great deal from product to product.

The life span of a product is affected by three main factors.

- **Technological change**

   This could cause a product to be replaced almost overnight by a new, more advanced version. Alternatively, advances in the way the product is manufactured and the discovery of new materials could lead to a new updated version being produced that has an improved performance.

- **Consumer demand**

   Demand for a product can change for a variety of reasons. It could become unfashionable or be regarded as unsafe or not being environmentally friendly. It may also become less popular if market competition is increased and new more attractive products are produced.

- **Company policy**

   A company may decide to kill off a product in order to make way for a new product or make use of new developments. This may be part of an overall economic strategy to remove choice from the consumer.

Typically a new product will progress through four stages in its life from when it is first introduced to the market place to when it is removed from sale. The graph below shows these stages and how sales might be affected over a period of time. It is important to realise that the time span at each stage will often be different and that sales figures can fluctuate depending on the time of year. However the graph is a useful way to show what will happen to a product and illustrate when a company should consider releasing an updated or newer model onto the market.

A Typical Product Life Cycle

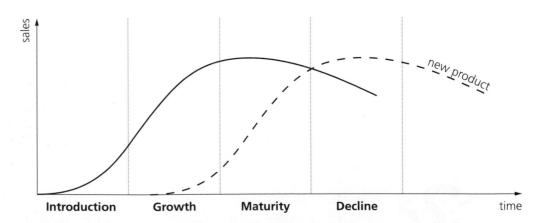

Introduction

This is the most expensive stage. The costs of design, development, marketing and production have not yet been recovered. In addition, further costs are incurred through advertising. The commercial viability of the product will be assessed during this stage.

Growth

Here the product is becoming established in the marketplace and sales outlets increase. Profits are realised as sales increase. Profits should be reinvested in developing new products. Competitors may enter the marketplace and a much wider range becomes available to the consumer.

Maturity

As competition becomes established and other similar products become available, sales will begin to drop. The market may have become saturated i.e. everyone who is likely to want one will have one. At this point, the company should be ready to launch a newer updated version of the product.

Decline

Sales fall dramatically. The product may be withdrawn from sale, especially if it appears to be in competition with their new product or if it is seen to damage the company's image in any way. The product may also have gone out of fashion.

The growth in personal computers in recent times has caused fierce competition between companies. Apple computers have a distinctive appearance that sets them apart from their rivals. However appearance alone will not guarantee future sales and the technical specification of their computers must continually be updated and improved to keep them competitive. The enormous capabilities of some home computers often remain redundant, as most home users have no need for such powerful machines. However new updated products keep being produced on an all-too-regular basis making perfectly good machines obsolete in the eyes of consumers.

In 1997 Apple released the Proforma 5500 series which was their first 'all-in-one' computer since the original Mac Classic produced in 1984. This was replaced in 1998 by the more fashionable imac. In 2002 the imac underwent a huge cosmetic transformation as well as providing the user with an improved technical specification and enhanced performance. As each new version was introduced so the sales for the previous model dropped. Apple were soon to remove from sale the older model, which many users found more than adequate. By doing this they removed the possibility of the older machine competing against the newer model.

The Mac classic designed by Apple computers 1984.

Proforma 5500   flat screen iMac   original iMac

Product Life Analysis

The creation of a new product requires a variety of people, other than the intended end user, to interact with it. People, such as those who make, assemble, package and repair it, all need to handle and use the product. It is therefore essential that the designer considers the needs of these people during the design process and establishes appropriate product requirements for each of them.

A good example of the importance of this is the repair and maintenance of a product. How often have you heard it said that a product is difficult to repair because the correct tool cannot be found or that the part needing to be repaired is inaccessible?

During each stage of a product's life, its human, environmental and economic requirements should be considered and investigated. This approach to product design is often referred to as **the cradle** (raw material production) **to grave** (its end of life disposal) approach.

The diagram below gives an indication of the main stages to be considered in the cradle to grave approach.

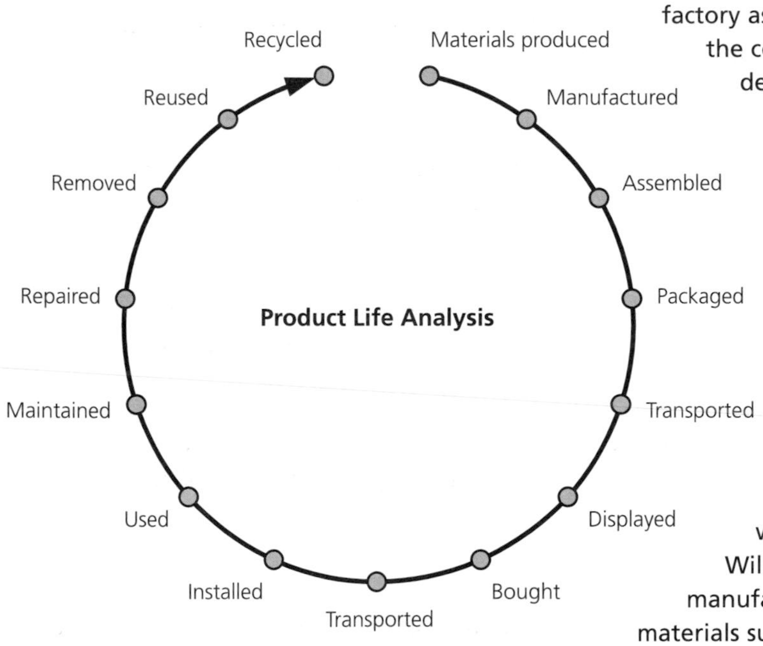

By examining the life cycle of a product from the time it enters the factory as raw materials to the time when it is discarded by the consumer for recycling or disposed of as waste, the designer is forced to think about how well the product will perform at each of these life cycle stages. This cradle to grave approach or whole design approach is much more sympathetic to the needs of everyone who interacts with the product.

Let us examine more closely some of the issues that should be considered at each of these stages.

Recycled
Reused
Removed
Repaired
Maintained
Used
Installed
Transported
Bought
Displayed
Transported
Packaged
Assembled
Manufactured
Materials produced

Product Life Analysis

Materials produced

Are these materials recyclable? How will using these materials affect the environment and workers? Can we afford the cost of these materials? Will these materials be suitable for the type of manufacturing required? Are the properties of the chosen materials suitable for the function of the product?

Manufactured

How long will it take to manufacture the product? What is the cost of manufacture? What restrictions will the method of manufacture impose on the design? i.e. wall thickness, radius corners, strength, appearance, etc.

Assembled

How will the product be assembled? Should the product be able to be disassembled at a later date? Should specialised tools be used for assembly and disassembly? (Useful for security and safety)

Packaged

Does the product require additional protection? Should the packaging be used to advertise and sell the product? What will happen to the packaging once the customer has finished with it?

Transported

Will the product require special conditions when being transported to the retail outlet? Is there a risk of the product being damaged during transportation?

Displayed

Should the product be displayed in direct sunlight? How well will the product compete alongside other similar product types in a shop? What is the risk of the product being damaged during display?

Bought

What are the selling features that will encourage a customer to buy the product? What benefits does the product offer?

Transported

Will the customer have any difficulty in transporting the product home? Does the product have any special requirements during transportation? i.e. must remain upright, must not be shaken, etc.

Installed

What expertise is required to install or prepare the product before using it? Does the user need access to the product for batteries, discs, plugs etc. before using it?

Used

Is the product easy to use? Is the product comfortable to use? Is the product safe to use? What level of abuse might the product be expected to take?

Maintained

Who is expected to maintain the product? What access is required to maintain the product? How will the product be cleaned, emptied, filled, powered, adjusted, etc?

Repaired

Who is expected to repair the product? What is likely to need repairing over time? What access will be required to repair the product? What parts should be available to repair the product?

Removed

Are there any laws over who can dispose of the product? (Consider CFCs, PCBs, chemicals, emissions and pollution). Will it cost money to have the product disposed of?

Reused

Can the product be reused or reconditioned? Can any parts be reclaimed and reused? Could the product be used as something else?

Recycled

Are all the parts able to be recycled? Are all the parts clearly identified for recycling? What facilities are required for these parts to be recycled?

Each of these stages can also act as a stimulus for writing the design specification and as a starting point for the evaluation and testing of the product.

Revise as you go!

- *What is meant by the 'cradle to grave' approach to designing products?*
- *Make a list of all the people who will come into contact with a mobile phone starting at the assembly stage.*

Planned Obsolescence

Planned obsolescence is a strategy used by companies and designers to cause products to be perceived as obsolete before they actually need to be replaced. This can be done in three ways.

- Create a fashion change or a demand for a new style.
- Hold back attractive functional features then introduce them on a later model, making the previous one obsolete.
- Produce products that will break, wear, tear or rot before they should.

It is difficult to get companies and designers to admit to deliberate company policies that would encourage any of these approaches. This would attract poor publicity and contradict many policies on sustainability issues. Designers and manufacturers have therefore to strike a balance between keeping the sales of their goods high and offering value-for-money, durable products that satisfy customers' desires to own the latest, most fashionable goods.

Often they respond by saying that consumers like style changes. They argue that people want new looks in fashion and demand goods that give them a feel-good factor. They defend themselves by saying that nobody has to buy the new look and, if it fails, they are the ones who will lose money.

Technological developments continually offer electronic goods with more features, more power and more variety. Therefore it is a fact that a product's features and functions will evolve over time. However is it right that a company holds back on these? They will say that they do so at their own risk, knowing that competitors may introduce features before them and steal the market.

Companies also argue that they only put in new materials to keep their costs and prices down and so are able to pass these savings on to the consumer. They do not want their products to break down prematurely because they do not want to lose their customers to other brands and develop a bad reputation.

Successful companies should consider a programme of **planned obsolescence** if they are to remain competitive in today's global marketplace. Consumers now expect products to evolve. They demand new improved technology and cosmetic change on a regular basis.

Many young people are very fashion conscious particularly when it comes to clothes, mobile phones and accessories. Designers are aware of this, so they design products with a fashionable appearance, which almost guarantees that it will look out of fashion in a year or two. This is known as building in **style obsolescence**. The concept of style obsolescence is becoming more important in a market place where consumer expectations of products are for longevity and reliability. However many find themselves buying new models of products when there is no functional or mechanical reason for doing so. Many products begin to look outdated before they actually break down. This is a conscious strategy on the part of the designer.

Bigger Picture

Electronics companies continue to develop new models at a more rapid and frequent rate. This creates difficulties in obtaining spare parts and dealers often refuse to repair outdated models.

The consumer finds that their new product quickly becomes out of date and it is harder to get it repaired. Gradually the manufacturer is putting pressure on the consumer to replace the old one.

The other side of the coin is a shifting attitude towards sustainable design: some large companies are now making a play of their 'green credentials' – perhaps in order to raise the perceived value of their goods?

Revise as you go!

- *Using examples describe the concept of obsolescence with regard to product design.*
- *What effect does designed obsolescence have on*
    - *(a) the consumer*
    - *(b) the environment?*

Redundancy

The last 25 years have seen a huge increase in the availability and use of advanced technology in consumer products. Most kitchens are now full of sophisticated and specialised machines and products. Cars have central computer systems controlling their performance and many have the capability to exceed the national speed limit by almost three times. Domestic hi-fi systems have sound capacities well beyond that acceptable in any living room and home computers have processors which are faster than the majority of home users will ever need or, more importantly, from which they will ever feel the benefit.

This extra power or extra capacity is referred to as **redundancy**. Redundancy is often built into a product as a marketing tool or a selling feature.

For example, how often have we heard of or read manufacturers' literature boasting that their new sports car has a top speed of 180 miles per hour and can go from 0 to 60 miles per hour in under 8 seconds? This extra speed and power is used as a marketing tool and is aimed at a group of consumers who feel that these features are important to their image and status or that they perhaps fulfil some other psychological need.

Additional capacity, strength or power is essential if a product is to withstand extreme conditions, abuse or misuse and still function well. Redundancy is an important design feature which should be considered for all products. However, the designer should be aware of the consequences of misuse of this redundant power while recognising the importance of the individual consumer's demand to fulfil a psychological need.

Designers and safety regulators need to set an agreed level of redundancy for products, i.e. a level of power or capacity over and above normal requirements.

Three questions need to be considered here:

■ Should a product be able to do other things (or more of the same) beyond its declared capabilities?

■ Should a product be safe in conditions other than those for which it has been designed to be used?

■ How safe should the product be in the hands of untrained, unskilled and unsupervised users?

Most households today have a washing machine. On average each machine will contain around twenty programmes. Most households only ever use about 25% of the programmes available. At the point of sale these extra facilities are used as a selling feature.

Consumers are now able to purchase powerful machines without any prior training in their use. Some will abuse and misuse them, or use them in ways never intended by the manufacturer. Injuries, accidents and product breakages are often the result. This highlights the need for designers to carefully consider issues such as building in a safety system beyond that required by the product in reasonable use, and designing products which are fit for the purpose intended.

The Subaru Impreza WRX Sti has a turbocharged 2.0-litre engine which accelerates from 0 to 60 mph in 5.45 seconds generating 195kW of power at 6,000rpm and 343Nm of torque at 4,000rpm. It has a top speed of around 150mph. The speed limit on the motorway today is 70mph. Why do you think the car has been given this extra power capability?

The apple iPod has taken personal music players to a new level. It has a 40GB hard drive able to hold up to 10,000 songs. That is four weeks of music played continuously for 24 hours a day or one new song every day for the next 27 years. The battery life for an iPod is less than 10 hours before needing to be recharged.

Revise as you go!

- *What is meant by the term 'redundancy'?*
- *Give one example where redundancy could be described as a safety feature in a product.*

Fashion and Style

Many people find it difficult to explain the difference between a fashion and a style. A distinction would be that things can come in and out of fashion but a style is something that is distinctive and will always exist. However, it may be more useful to describe each separately and then to compare the two.

Bigger Picture

Sometimes referred to as Rubix Cube, this toy had its time during the early 1980s. During 1982 sales had reached over 100 million. By the summer of 1983 the Rubik's Cube fad was over and production had ceased. It made a small comeback during the 1990s selling around 500,000 units.

Fashion

A **fashion** is something that is current. It is something that has been accepted as being popular by a group of consumers and will remain so for a period of time. Fashionable products, such as fashionable clothes, pass through many stages. At first, a small number of consumers take an interest in something that sets them apart and makes them feel different from others. This often happens with celebrities or sports stars. During the mid-1990s, a small number of famous football players began to wear coloured football boots. Next, the fashion becomes popular and is adopted by the mass market. This was highlighted by an explosion in the number of coloured football boots worn by young boys to the point where it became unusual to see any football team where all the players wore black boots. Finally, the fashion begins to fade and consumers move towards other things that catch their eye. Although coloured football boots can still be bought, it is more usual now for black boots to be worn. The demand for coloured boots has faded.

Revise as you go!

- *Discuss, using examples, the difference between fashion and style.*
- *List two products that are currently in fashion.*
- *What do you think may cause them to go out of fashion?*

Style

A **style** is more distinctive and can be classed as a mode of expression. For example, there are instantly recognisable styles of architecture such as Georgian, Victorian and Art Deco. Art also has recognisable styles such as surrealism, abstractionism, or expressionism, and although clothing can go through many fashion changes, styles of clothing can still be classified as formal, casual or sporting.

Fads

We should also consider **fads** as being of interest to designers and manufacturers. The term 'fad' denotes a product that becomes fashionable very quickly and is adopted with great enthusiasm by certain market groups but declines in popularity after a short time. Young people in particular are attracted to this type of product. Good examples are electronic pets, yo-yos and cabbage patch dolls. Fads do not survive long because they do not fulfil any real need or offer any real benefit to the consumer.

The following illustrations give an indication of how the life cycle of a product might appear, if it were an item of fashion, style or a fad.

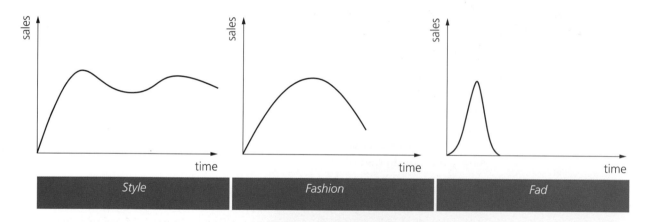

| Style | Fashion | Fad |

© MAIMAN RICK/CORBIS SYGMA

Swatch watches were first produced in 1983. They became a fashion accessory which reflected the style of the 80s. Swatch was marketed as a lifestyle product – a fashion accessory for the young design-conscious consumer. The chairman of Swatch said of the product 'Everyone needs more than one Swatch. They need two, three, four because it is not so much a watch as a fashion accessory.' The watch was made with a limited number of components at an affordable price. The lead time to production was very short which allowed the company to keep pace with changes in fashion.

Safety

Safety is vital to the success of any product design. Products today are generally much safer than they were many years ago and this is partly the result of consumer group pressure as well as improved testing and quality control by manufacturers. Products today are designed to meet regulations set by the **BSI** (British Standards Institution) and the **ISO** (International Standards Organisation). Part of the remit of these institutions is to assess risk and the likelihood of accident or damage to people and property. These risks may involve:

- a risk to the health and safety of humans
- a risk to the environment
- a risk to the product
- any potential risks due to a delay in the product's operation or its complete failure.

Safety proofing of products is an expensive task. It may be impossible to make a product completely risk free when it is being abused or used wrongly. Therefore, legislation, bylaws or agreed performance standards are set by professional bodies to determine acceptable levels of performance and safety.

Designers may face dilemmas between satisfying popular consumer demands for product performance and satisfying their own responsibilities with regard to safety, the environment and professional ethics. For example, product safety in cars cannot be guaranteed if the consumer values speed and power more than safety features. Air bags, side impact bars, anti-locking brakes and every other built-in safety feature will be ineffective if the car has a head-on collision at 130 miles per hour. Although plastic pen tops are designed so that they are open at both ends, there can be no absolute guarantee that someone will not choke on one, if it is swallowed. Both of these examples involve products being used wrongly, although their designers have built in safety features in case of accidents.

Responsible manufacturers want to produce safe products which still have market appeal. The way a company deals with product quality and safety problems can damage or help its reputation. A company selling products that are unsafe or do not meet the standards set down by law may face legal action resulting in hefty compensation payments. Also, many consumers who are unhappy with a product may begin to avoid buying other products produced by the same company and may persuade other consumers to do likewise.

Safety is obviously so important that it should feature throughout the design and development of a product and not be regarded as something that is bolted on at the end.

Every product will become dangerous in the wrong hands and a designer has no control over how it will be used or what it will be used for once it is bought. However, they must build in safety features to prevent accidents and try to anticipate how those who may come into contact with the product will use and perhaps abuse it.

Revise as you go!

- *Write down six safety considerations that should be made in the design of power tools to safeguard anyone who comes into contact with them.*
- *Explain why the safety of children should be considered in the design of all household products even though only adults are meant to use them.*

The following questions may help:

- How safe will the product be in the hands of children and other inexperienced users?

- Is the user going to be at risk if the product fails, breaks down or does not fulfil its function properly?

- Will the product become more dangerous to use if it is mistreated, misused, dropped or thrown?

- Is the product likely to become more dangerous if it is exposed to a change in operating conditions, for example caused by weather, resulting in exposure to extreme hot or cold, water, moisture or humidity?

Bottle tops that require to be pushed and twisted before they can be opened make it more difficult for young children to get access to the contents.

Power tools which are to be used outdoors must be double insulated.

Many electrical products now require a special tool to allow access to parts that might need to be repaired or replaced. This will discourage DIY enthusiasts attempting a home repair that might make the product less safe.

New materials and a redesign of the method used to attach the flex to an iron have all but eliminated the risk caused by frayed and worn flexes.

Technological Opportunity

Technology plays an important part in our lives today. Almost everything we see, touch and use has been affected by some form of technology. Medicine, computers, transport, clothes, food and everyday domestic products are now being manufactured, developed and improved using technology that did not exist 20 years ago.

New Technology

Every new technology replaces an older one and companies who ignore the opportunities provided by new technology can often find their business declining and their products overtaken by newer versions. For example, developments in laser technology and its application to domestic products resulted in the compact disc player, which very quickly began to replace vinyl records and record players. This new technology provided the opportunity for the design and development of the Discman, a small portable CD player.

New technologies can create new markets and provide opportunities for new products. Companies strive to keep up with the pace of technological change and those who do not may very soon find their products outdated. The life spans of these new products are becoming shorter as consumers' demands and expectations rise. Examples of this can be found in products such as mobile telephones and computers where new models are being introduced into the market only months after their predecessors.

Technology Transfer

Developments in technology in unrelated industries can also affect the fortunes of a company. The growth of electronic components and the inexpensive way in which they are now produced has led their manufacturers to look for new applications, new markets and new uses for them. We now see what were once regarded as expensive components appearing in children's toys, novelty ties, watches and even Christmas cards.

The high cost of researching, developing and introducing new technologies has meant that companies concentrate much of their efforts into making minor improvements, such as introducing new features and styles, to their products. They may also look for opportunities to transfer new technology, which has already been developed and tested in other products, into their product range.

Opportunities to Use New Technology

Companies and designers must actively look for opportunities to use new technology otherwise their products will begin to look dated and perhaps be regarded as obsolete.

Essentially there are four broadly similar methods which can be used to identify opportunities to incorporate new technology into existing and new products.

1   Analyse competing products to look for any example of new technology or innovation. It is important to know what the competition is up to. This should be done by an expert in the relevant technological field who can closely examine

similar products produced by other companies. Obviously patents, copyrights and other forms of **intellectual property** must be observed.

2   Keep as informed as possible about technological developments in other areas of industry. This may lead to **technology transfer** or stimulate further developments which can lead to an existing technology being adapted for use in a different product type.

3   Establish links with universities and research centres to keep informed about possible new and emerging technologies. In-depth information about new technology is normally best sought from experts in the relevant field. Many experts have their work published in journals and magazines or exhibit at conferences and exhibitions.

4   Attempt to forecast future technological trends. Many designers refer to this as 'Blue Sky' thinking. This approach encourages creativity without having the constraints of today's technology. It may stimulate new ideas which could in turn encourage scientists, engineers and research centres to develop technology in a new way.

Materials development is an area of technology that can provide opportunities to improve existing products. The material used to coat these pans was originally developed for space research.

The processor used in this Game Boy would have been able to power a small personal computer a few years ago.

Revise as you go!

● *Give two of your own examples of products that have been developed as a result of technological opportunity. Justify your answers.*

● *What is meant by the term 'technology transfer'?*

Fitness for Purpose

Evaluating and testing products often means working to strict criteria and finding answers to a broad range of questions. Possibly the most important question that needs to be answered is 'How well does the product do its job?' In other words we need to know how fit the product is for the purpose for which it was designed.

Everyday objects can be very frustrating if they do not work, or do not work as well as we had hoped. Is this because we cannot use them properly, because they do not work well or because we are using them for something they were not designed to do?

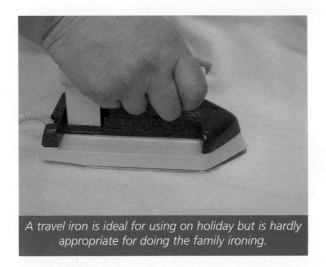

A travel iron is ideal for using on holiday but is hardly appropriate for doing the family ironing.

A travel iron is small, compact and lightweight, and may have folding parts or attachments that make it easy to store. However, its performance is not as efficient as a top-of-the range household iron and it will not cope well with many of the items in a normal household wash. It was designed to cope with lightweight shirts, T-shirts and other items of holiday clothing and would probably be expected to be used infrequently, possibly without a traditional ironing board.

The household iron and the travel iron carry out similar functions but are designed to be used in different situations and under different conditions. The expectations for these two products are quite different. Both do their own jobs well but neither could fulfil all the tasks and meet all the desired functions of the other.

When considering **fitness for purpose**, the designer should be clear about what the product must do, where it is likely to be used and who is likely to be using it. All the essential and desirable features of the product should be clearly established at the start of the design process and then checked at the end.

Camping is a popular activity which can require people to carry equipment and luggage over long distances. A camping stove is an essential item especially if a prolonged period out in the open is planned. The specification for a camping stove would have to include using lightweight materials, making the stove as small as possible with an emphasis on making the product safe. There are many interesting designs available on the market, as the camping stove has challenged the designer for years.

A camping stove and kettle.

Campers do not expect the same level of performance from a camping stove as they would from a kitchen cooker. It will take longer to cook food and users will not have the same level of control over heat. However the stove is fit for its purpose and should not be compared to a family kitchen cooker. Neither product could do the other product's job.

Using advanced technology to design sports equipment can lead to a spectacular improvement in performance. Mike Burrows in collaboration with Lotus Engineering designed this racing bicycle. It has a one-piece aerodynamic frame made from carbon fibres in an epoxy resin matrix. The pedals and the handlebars were made from titanium. The back wheel is attached to the frame using an integrated suspension system. A one-piece fork made from carbon fibre is used to hold the front wheel. The bicycle was designed for racing and it would hardly be appropriate to use it for any other purpose.

© Mike King/CORBIS

The Lotus Pursuit Bicycle

Revise as you go!

- *Describe what is meant by the term 'fitness for purpose'.*
- *Give two examples of products that are fit for purpose but would perform or function badly if used in the wrong circumstances.*

Social Responsibilities

The most well-known design movements and groups of the last century include Art Nouveau, Art Deco, Bauhaus, Modernism, Post-Modernism and Memphis. Each of them has played a part in creating the market-led economy in which we live. Today's product designers are faced with the enormous challenge of designing products to meet the needs and wants of consumers while still being socially responsible in their work.

Big business and clever marketing techniques are influencing our lifestyles, values and interests. Styles, fashions and fads are being created through the mass media – television and the popular press are two of the main contributors. Designers are being employed to respond to this by designing products and creating styles which will bring profit and popularity to their clients. In itself, this is not wrong – every designer has a responsibility to his or her employers or clients. However, designers also have much wider responsibilities to the people who use their products and to the environment.

Waste, pollution, dwindling natural resources and unwanted by-products are all caused by manufacturing. Designers should aim to minimise the environmental impact of their work and should consider the social consequences of introducing new products into the marketplace. For example, priority could be given to designing consumer products that use less energy, last longer and are able to be recycled. However, designers' priorities are normally determined by market demand. Products that are socially and environmentally desirable may prove to have no market demand. Therefore such products may never be produced.

There are many opportunities to design products for the benefit of society that can be explored by examining life around us. Examples include:

- disabled people
- medical equipment
- old people
- survival equipment
- research and laboratory equipment
- animal welfare.

There is also a need for designers to consider the risks arising from products being used in the wrong way or by people who have not been sufficiently trained. Power tools, cars, electrical goods and even children's toys can cause serious injury if they are used carelessly or misused. Design should be about improving quality of life. It should be a problem-solving activity, not a problem-creating one.

There are many social and moral issues that influence which products consumers decide to buy. Many are now taking an active interest in the wider issues related to design and manufacturing. Four examples of this are:

1   Many consumers are concerned about animal welfare and will not buy a product if it has been tested on animals or if animals have been mistreated during the development stages.

2   Consumers are now protesting against the exploitation of labour in the developing world. Some products that are designed in Europe and America are manufactured elsewhere because labour costs are cheaper. Many workers in the developing world are forced to work long hours in poor conditions for low wages.

3   Consumers are now looking to buy products which they can recycle at the end of the product's life.

4   Some consumers will not buy a product if it has been made in a material that is not sustainable.

Designers and companies are responding to these concerns. They realise that the products they produce need to be socially and environmentally acceptable. This social responsibility has been consumer led and designers are in a unique position to influence change. They are a link between the product, the company and the consumer. As such they have a responsibility to influence the decisions made by companies and can encourage them to respond to consumers' concerns and become socially and ethically responsible.

A designer will use many skills and strategies throughout the process of designing products. Their approach to their work can be creative, evaluative and analytical but whatever the outcome their work should be socially responsible and contribute to sustainable development.

Bigger Picture

The Body Shop produce a range of cosmetics and accessories which according to their own website 'use environmentally sustainable resources wherever technically and environmentally possible'. They use minimal packaging and encourage consumers to refill and recycle their products.

Revise as you go!

- *Give two examples of how both the designer and the consumer could act in a more socially responsible way.*

- *How can product designers influence clients and consumers to be more socially responsible?*

Product Evolution

Product development is usually the result of small changes and modifications being made to a particular product type. This step-by-step type of evolution is known as **incremental** (gradual, step-by-step) **change**. The result of any change can be an improved product or, in some cases, a different product. Many examples will spring to mind when you consider the products you encounter in everyday life.

The domestic iron has undergone many changes from the time when it was no more than a flat, shaped piece of metal that was heated over an open fire and used with a cloth around the handle to prevent burning. Over the years, it has gradually seen the introduction of new plastic materials, electric elements, electric cables, thermostats, power indicators, water level indicators, water spray devices and lightweight metal alloys with non-stick plates, to name but a few.

These changes did not happen all at once and are the result of over one hundred years of evolution. Many of the changes were the result of technological developments in other products and areas, but all were applied to the iron after identifying a **user need** or **weakness** in the product.

By going back to the early stages of the problem and thinking it through afresh, it is possible to redefine what the need is for the product. In the case of an iron, it would be reasonable to assume that its purpose is to iron out the wrinkles and creases in clothes. However, in some cases maybe an iron is not the best answer. For example, a trouser press offers a completely different solution that uses similar technology to that of an iron. This type of product development can be referred to as **radical change** – the product being designed is radically different from the expected norm.

Other factors that can influence radical change in product development are discoveries in new materials and new technologies. Although plastic did not make a radical difference to the design of the iron, it did make a huge difference to the way it was produced and the way it was used. It was soon to become an easily mass-produced product which was affordable by the majority. It is much lighter than its Victorian predecessor and able to be used much more efficiently.

Product evolution is often slow because the things that cause change to happen take time to develop,

'Highly Evolved' – the latest Sony widescreen TV manufactured in 2004.

Revise as you go!

- *Use an example of a product to describe incremental change.*
- *Write down three things that can cause a product to evolve in some way.*

test and apply. Some of the factors that contribute to product evolution are listed below.

- Developments in materials
- Developments in electronics
- Improved manufacturing techniques
- Legislation

A technological discovery that can be applied or adapted for use in products.

When Sony produced its first widescreen model in 1995 it represented cutting edge technology with its flat wide screen. Today televisions look similar but the technology that makes them work has evolved considerably since 1995. Digital televisions with surround sound, split screens and access to the internet are now available and becoming increasingly commonplace.

The way we record television programmes and play back movies has evolved so much that the video recorder is almost obsolete technology. Like most products its evolution has been slow since it first appeared in 1971. They remained bulky objects with limited functions and features until the 1990s. By then manufacturers could make them smaller with a more streamlined appearance. They had a multitude of features including ni-cam stereo, remote control, and bar code programming as well as the ability to be set to record weeks in advance. Recordable DVD players are now available and will soon take over completely from the video recorder.

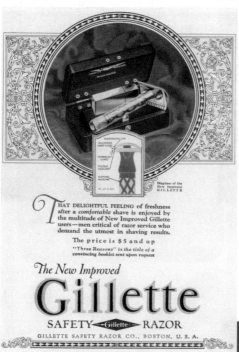

Of course it is not only hi-tech products that are evolving. Developments in materials and methods of manufacture have improved the appearance and functional qualities of many other product types as well as making them cheaper to produce.

Philips N-1500 video recorder manufactured in 1971.

In 1904 King C. Gillette was granted a patent for the first safety razor. Up until that point technical experts had told this travelling salesman that it would be impossible to produce steel that was hard, thin and inexpensive enough for the commercial development of the razor. The company has grown since then and now produces razors with triple blades, swivel head, and lubricating strip in a plastic moulded handle designed to fit snugly into the hand.

The King Camp Gillette safety razor 1904 made from metal.

Case Study

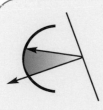

Bang and Olufsen have been producing quality home entertainment systems since 1925. Visit their website at **www.bang-olufsen.com** and read about how their products have evolved up to the present day.

Product Types

Every product has a unique style and image. Products may perform the same function, but under strictly controlled testing it is likely that differences will be found in areas such as efficiency, power and user-friendliness.

It is not uncommon to refer to groups of products as being of the same '**product type**'. For example, cylindrical vacuum cleaners, upright vacuum cleaners, carpet sweepers, carpet shampoo cleaners and hand-held vacuum cleaners can all be regarded as being of the same product type. These products all perform similar functions: they clean carpets, floors and other surfaces.

Design development quite often relies on designers examining these product types and making small modifications to existing products. By undergoing such step-by-step changes and improvements, products can evolve. This evolution sometimes results in quite different products. Today's cordless electric kettles are vastly different from the flat-bottomed kettles that used to stand on the hot tops of kitchen stoves in the late 19th century. The evolution of this product type has been well documented over the years and small incremental changes, together with advances in materials and technology, have seen it evolve to its present state. Will the same level of change take place over the next hundred years? What will the kettle of the future look like?

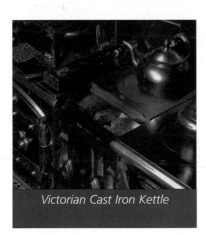

Victorian Cast Iron Kettle

Tefal Defina Gold Hi-Speed Kettle

Hot Berta Kettle by Philippe Starck

Revise as you go!

- *Compare the Victorian cast-iron kettle with the other two shown on the page opposite. What technological changes have made the changes in design possible?*

- *What does the term 'product type' mean? Use examples to illustrate your answer.*

Evolutionary development has resulted in a means of boiling water which is remarkably different to the method used in Victorian times. Even today however there are still kettles designed for use on the hob of a kitchen cooker. These are all **types** of products that boil water.

Evolution in one product type can sometimes lead to developments in a different product type or even to the development of a completely new product. Obvious examples include the developments in laser and microprocessor technologies for military and medical purposes, which have led to changes in home and leisure products. CD players, Discman and MP3 players, which have come about because of such research, are now considered everyday product types.

Radio and television has evolved in a much shorter time span. Developments have also been closely linked to advances in technology and in the range of new materials that have became available. The radio of today is quite different to early models but interestingly some manufacturers are producing high-tech models with retro styling.

Portable radios all perform the same basic function. People listen to the radio almost as much as they watch television. Portable radios are now lightweight and provide good sound quality – they all have the same basic functions. Although they can be said to be the same type of product they all have different features incorporated into their design, such as an alarm, illuminated dials, methods of tuning, digital or analogue, battery or mains power.

Case Study

Seymour Powell have been designing products since the early 1980s. Visit their website at **www.seymourpowell.co.uk** and find an example of a product type that they have designed over the years. Record these in your file and write down how you feel the product has evolved.

Miniaturisation

Many years ago, before the transistor was first developed, electronic products were big and cumbersome. The potential of the transistor began to be realised in the late 1950s and early 1960s. However it had been with us since around 1948. At that time radios required thermonic valves to function. These were large electronic components in the form of gas-filled glass globes. The outer appearance of these early products was dictated by their internal components and they were generally made to look like items of furniture. Developments in microelectronics, in particular the microchip, have resulted in significant changes to electronic goods. Products are now much smaller, saving resources and allowing much greater choice and freedom for the consumer.

The race to put a man on the moon during the 1960s accelerated developments in microchip technology. Computers began to become more powerful but they were still huge machines occupying several rooms. Products are now able to be manufactured which are much smaller, giving more scope to the designer.

Everyday products, such as computers, televisions and telephones, are much smaller than they were fifty years ago – pocket-sized versions of each are becoming more common. The shape and size of these products is no longer controlled by large, bulky components. Products are much lighter, more flexible and more powerful than ever before. However, this trend towards miniaturisation is making reclaiming and recycling of parts and materials more difficult. Mass-produced products are now proving cheaper to replace than to repair.

In some instances, miniaturisation has resulted in some products being regarded as cheap and not desirable. During the 1970s and 1980s, increased importing from the Far East of such products as small radios, watches and calculators resulted in these products becoming widely available and so very disposable. The value of these products was reduced, and designers became aware that they were no longer designing 'precious' products.

The Japanese with their inherent culture of simplicity and minimalism embraced new technology at an early stage. They now lead the world in the development and production of electronic products. This is nowhere better illustrated than by the Sony Corporation. By 1958 Sony had reduced the transistor radio to about the size of an average shirt pocket. During the 1980s they had developed the Walkman, which had an unprecedented effect on the culture of that time. The company continues to grow and today they are at the forefront of electronic product development.

Early Radios looked like the furniture of the time, housing much larger components than similar products of today. The famous round EKCO radio was in production between 1934 and 1945. The bakelite 'cabinet' was designed by Wells Coates and was available in various colours. Consumers at the time preferred the walnut finish.

The Effects of Miniaturisation

Developments in microelectronics have affected the product designer and the consumer in several ways since the 1950s:

■ Miniaturisation of working parts has meant much greater freedom for designers. Products' external forms are no longer restricted by large working parts.

■ The cost of small electronic products continues to reduce as mass-production techniques improve and the technological capabilities of microchips increase.

■ The recycling and reuse of these small electronic products is becoming more difficult and less cost-effective.

The growth in microelectronics and the development of computer chips and printed circuit boards means that computers can be much smaller than ever before. The now familiar laptop computer can outperform a computer that filled two rooms 25 years ago.

Sony made the radio cassette player a reality. Personal, private and portable stereo music became available to everyone. The Walkman became an icon representing freedom, individuality and youth.

Revise as you go!

● *List ten products that have benefited from miniaturisation.*

● *Give an example of two products that are now able to combine features and functions as a result of miniaturisation.*

Systems Diagrams

When designing any product, it is important to have some understanding of how it works. The first step in this is to identify the **inputs** and desired **outputs** of the product. The processes that allow this to happen are not important, particularly in the early stages. This approach is often described as the 'Black Box' approach.

These three areas of product design, inputs, process and outputs, combine to give us the **Universal System**.

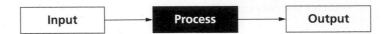

From this basic system, we can begin to explore possible inputs and outputs to our product. This can also form part of the creative design process. For example, consider the design of a mobile telephone. Possible inputs to the system may include:

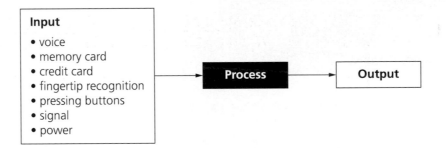

Of course, there are many other inputs that could be considered in a mobile telephone, each in itself forming the basis of some investigation and research work. A similar brainstorming exercise can be carried out on the possible outputs.

Once all the inputs and outputs have been decided upon, the designer will have a clear indication of all the product functions and features, and can begin the process of designing the buttons, switches, sockets, clips, screens, lights, slots, batteries or speakers that will be included in any proposed solution.

This will form the basis for discussions with electronic engineers, materials technologists, production engineers, marketing departments, graphic designers, and sales and distribution teams both before and after fully rendered proposals are made.

As the planning for the phone develops, the systems diagram approach can be used to describe more fully how the product might work.

Consider a pupil's system diagram of a mobile phone. This was written during the design stage of a project where he was asked to design a mobile phone that would appeal to the 18–25 age group.

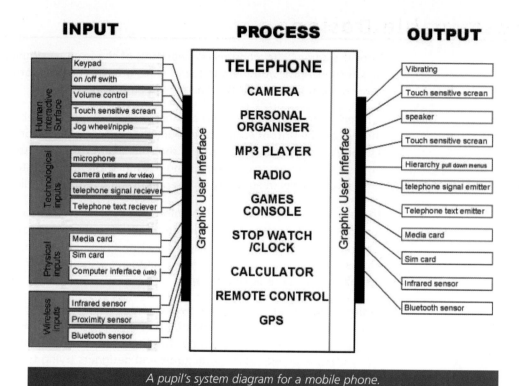

A pupil's system diagram for a mobile phone.

The pupil has divided up the possible inputs into four categories;

1   The human interactive surface would require the user to physically make contact with the phone.

2   Technological inputs would require another product to interact with it.

3   Physical inputs will require the user to put something into or onto the phone.

4   Wireless inputs will require the phone to be able to sense different type of signals.

A similar exercise should be carried out for the output side of the diagram. Breaking down the inputs and outputs in this way will enable the designer to clearly see what sort of physical features will need to be included on the external surface of the phone.

It is likely that an electronics engineer would be required to design the processing board to fulfil all the requirements of the phone. Throughout this stage both the electronics engineer and the designer would communicate regularly to discuss the product's technical and performance requirements.

Today, product design is a team effort, with experts from various fields and disciplines contributing to the product designer's work. In the early stages of the design process, a simple **systems diagram** will help everyone to focus on what the product will do and how it might perform.

Revise as you go!

•   *Explain what is meant by the term 'Black Box technology'.*

•   *Produce a universal systems diagram for a hairdryer.*

Sustainable Design

Since the early 1980s, consumers' awareness of the issues surrounding '**green** design' began to increase, and there is now a much greater trend towards producing 'environmentally-friendly' products or 'green products'.

A recent report has suggested that more than 23 million household products are thrown out by Britons each year. Around 10 per cent of these products still functioned. Although many complain about the short lifespan of their household appliances, others say that they do not want long-lasting machines, preferring instead to regularly buy the newest model in an effort to 'keep up-to-date' with technology.

There is a growing consensus of opinion that problems affecting the environment cannot be ignored. People are now demonstrating their feelings by actions. Many are making conscious decisions to recycle and reuse products but, as the statement above suggests, this is still not enough. Many more are using environmental criteria in their purchasing decisions as consumers.

Designers and manufacturers are aware of this and some use 'green design' as a marketing tool. For example, one brand of washing-up liquid was labelled as being 'phosphate free' at a time when no washing-up liquid contained phosphates. There are many other examples of manufacturers and designers trying to increase sales using what could be described as a 'green con'.

The Designer's Responsibilities

Everyone has a responsibility to design and use products that are the result of 'environmentally-sensible design'. Many designers assume that their area of responsibility is limited to function and appearance but they also have a moral and social responsibility. There are two issues that should be considered:

- Should designers continue designing products with **built-in obsolescence** and **redundancy**?
- Should designers concentrate on addressing consumers' **needs** rather than **wants**?

As well as responding to these questions, responsible designers must begin to establish each of the following areas as important issues throughout the design process:

- Use recycled materials or materials from a sustainable source
  Designers should consider whether a recycled material would provide the same properties as a first generation material.

- Design products that can be recycled or re-used
  This can be made easier by using fewer different materials in the one product and labelling all the materials clearly.

Revise as you go!

- *List five products that have been designed to reduce the amount of energy they use compared to other similar products.*
- *Write down four ways that a designer could attempt to make a product more 'green'.*

- Choose materials carefully

  Choosing a sustainable material for the production of any product is essential if we are to safeguard our natural resources. Consideration must also be given to using biodegradable materials. Designers should also be careful not to use materials that will prove hazardous when being disposed of.

- Extend the product's life

  Design the product so as it is able to be maintained and serviced by ensuring components that are at risk of failure are easily accessible and able to be repaired.

- Use the minimum amount of material possible

  As well as the environmental benefits of saving resources there is a cost saving and less of a problem with the disposal of the product at the end of its useful life. Three possibilities exist here:

  (a) keeping the product simpler and lighter in weight

  (b) considering how to make the product smaller

  (c) producing products that perform more than one function.

The Green Product

In the quest for the 'Unachievable Green Product', designers and consumers should at least be able to ask the right questions of products before making a moral and social decision on whether to manufacture or buy it. These questions include:

- Is there a risk of disastrous failure?
- Could the product be cleaner?
- Is the product energy efficient?
- Could the product be quieter?
- Should the product be more intelligent?
- Is the product over-designed?
- How long will the product last?
- What will happen when the product's useful life is over?
- Can the product find an environmental market?
- Will it appeal to the green consumer?

Ten questions for the green designer (A booklet prepared for the Design Council) by John Elkington Associates, 1986

Bigger Picture

During the early nineties the German company AEG developed a new style of washing machine called the Lavamat which achieved low energy and water consumption through a sophisticated microprocessor and sensor system. Around the same time Zanussi developed the Nexus 'Jetstream RS' which had many of its parts made from a polymer based material called Carboran which is fully recyclable. This replaced a more conventional steel casing.

Social Behaviour

People's tastes differ. While this statement is true and each person can be regarded as an individual, on a global scale designers treat people in groups or 'segments' differentiated by such factors as cultural differences, religious beliefs, lifestyle or age. They will design products for particular market segments according to that group's perceived needs and wants.

Lifestyle is a huge factor in the types of products now being designed. People's lifestyles have changed remarkably, especially since the 1950s. Postwar affluence has allowed more people to own a variety of different types of products.

'There was a strange moment around the mid 1960s when people stopped needing and need changed to wants...'

Sir Terence Conran

Washing machines, microwaves and hairdryers are no longer regarded as luxury items. In fact they are essential for busy families where parents are working and time is at a premium. Parents may have to leave early in the morning and return late in the evening. There is little time to cook, clean the house and do the washing and so there is a demand for these 'time-saving' products.

Other families have found themselves with more time on their hands. Working from home, longer holidays, living locally and working shorter hours have all contributed to people having more time for leisure pursuits. As a result, we have seen a big rise in keep-fit products from training shoes to exercise machines.

Different kinds of social behaviour will lead to demands for different kinds of products. People behave differently and do different things at different times of the year. They respond to fashion trends differently and have to cope with changes in a country's economic climate. Designers have to be aware of how consumers react to these situations and be able to respond with marketable products.

Design and product development are now part of most company business plans. The types of products produced must change with the lifestyles and needs of consumers. These consumer needs can be affected by changes in the law, local customs, topical issues and current affairs, as well as by the factors in examples given above.

A consumer's behaviour is strongly influenced by cultural, social, personal and psychological characteristics.

Cultural Factors

Human behaviour to a large extent is learned from family, friends and other important institutions. Designers continually try to anticipate and spot cultural shifts in order to imagine new products that might be wanted. For example the increased desire for more leisure time has resulted in more demand for convenience and entertainment based products.

Social Factors

A consumer's behaviour is also influenced by their social status and other social factors like their circle of friends or organised groups of which they are members. Belonging to a group either formally or informally will influence a person's choice of product. Teenagers in particular form close associations with others in their peer group who like the same music or share a similar interest or hobby. This will often influence the products and clothes that they choose to buy. As they get older people begin to buy products that reflect their status in society.

Personal Factors

A consumer's choice of product is also influenced by personal circumstances such as age, occupation, economic situation, personality and lifestyle. As each of these circumstances will change through time so will the type of product that a person will buy.

Psychological Factors

The product a consumer buys is also strongly influenced by four psychological factors:

Modern kitchens are full of time-saving appliances to enable families to spend less time in the kitchen and more time pursuing other activities.

(i)   Motivation

Sometimes we are motivated to buy a product through a desire to be recognised, or be safe, or to recognise or reward someone.

(ii)   Perception

People perceive things differently. We often buy products because we perceive them to be of good quality. We also avoid buying certain products or going into certain shops because we perceive them to be inferior.

(iii)   Learning

Learning will often change a person's behaviour. This can be the result of an experience of actually doing something. If our experience of a product is a good one than we are more likely to develop a **brand loyalty** to its manufacturers. Equally, if our experience is not good then we are less likely to buy products made by the same company.

Many people hold the belief that Japanese companies are better at designing electronic products.

(iv)   Beliefs

Throughout their life people will acquire beliefs and attitudes. These in turn will influence their buying behaviour. A consumer may decide to buy a digital camera because they believe that it takes great photographs, will last a long time, is good value for money and can be fully recycled at the end of its useful life. These beliefs can be based on knowledge, experience or opinion. They may also hold the belief or attitude that electronic products made in Japan are of better quality than those made in Europe. This can also influence product choice. Attitudes and beliefs are often difficult to change and a designer will need to examine those of the target market closely before designing any new product.

Revise as you go!

- *Briefly describe two psychological factors that can influence the products we buy. Use examples of products to illustrate your answer.*
- *Describe how people's lifestyles can influence the products they buy.*

Consumer Expectations

Consumers are now much more aware of 'good design' than ever before. They expect products to function well, look good and remain competitive in a market where they are often spoilt for choice. They are more aware of their legal rights and of the legal restrictions and requirements demanded of consumer products. They have high expectations and demands of the goods they buy. Reliability, durability and user-friendliness must all be delivered at competitive prices and there is also an expectation that products will be 'environmentally friendly'. All of these things are brought to their attention by consumer watchdogs, reports, journals and other media. To some extent, consumers are told what is good design without having to run the risks of trying products for themselves.

The Expectation of Choice

Image and style are now important factors in consumer choice. Designers now regard consumers' tastes and desire to remain 'in vogue' as a priority. Gone are the days when you could have 'any colour so long as it was black'. Consumers expect choice, variety and change. This presents a challenge to designers, who have to compete in a global economy where most products will be mass produced. Mass production means that it is impossible to offer the variety and exclusivity of the types of products offered by small-scale or handmade production methods. Today consumers expect choice but are reluctant to pay more for it.

From the 1950s onwards, the British marketplace has slowly evolved from one of scarcity and need to one of abundance and choice. One can say that we now live in a market-led economy where consumers expect quality products that represent value for money. We also demand variety, which in turn has resulted in products changing and being updated more often. It is almost as if consumers build in their own 'style obsolescence'.

Questions for the Designer

When writing a specification for a new product it is common to think of its technical requirements, performance requirements and the product's market requirements. For each of these three areas a designer must consider what the consumer expects from the product. The difficulty for the designer is that not all consumers' expectations are the same, as each individual's needs, wants, values and desires differ. However a designer can begin to work around this by asking these three questions:

What **basic features** will the consumer demand from the product?

What **new features** will the consumer expect from the product to allow it to compete with other similar product types?

How many **unexpected features** can be introduced to this new product to give it a 'wow!' factor?

Expected Feature

There is a basic level of product features that a consumer expects without having to ask or pay extra for. If these features are not present then the consumer will be disappointed with the product. For example consumers now **expect** a new television to have a remote control. They would be disappointed to find that this wasn't provided as standard. However at this time they do not expect every television to have split screens and multi-channel viewing as standard. No doubt this or something similar will become standard as televisions evolve and this type of technology becomes less expensive.

Over time **unexpected features** will become **expected** features. The unexpected can only be unexpected once and gradually these features will be not only expected but eventually a basic requirement of that product.

When Sony released its Playstation 2, the improved graphics and new features caused excitement and delight among Playstation users. Prior to its release these users were perfectly happy with their original Playstation and did not express any dissatisfaction with the graphics or the product's features. It was not within most people's knowledge or experience to anticipate such an improvement in performance and therefore it was **unexpected**.

However there will be an expectation among users that the next generation of Playstations will provide a similar level of product improvement. This now puts pressure on Sony to develop the product beyond its existing capabilities.

The Sony Playstation 1 and Playstation 2

Revise as you go!
- *Explain how unexpected features in a new product will become expected features over time. Use products to illustrate your answer.*
- *Describe the factors that now influence consumer choice when buying products.*

Economic Considerations

When most people think about economics, they begin to think about the price of products. This is something that is determined by market forces and not something that a designer has much control over. How much someone is willing to pay for a product is determined by many things and is not necessarily controlled by the company which is selling it.

A good design idea may not always be economically viable. In most cases, this would mean that by the time the product's estimated maximum sales are reached the manufacturer will not have made enough income to exceed all the product's costs.

Resources

Good economic awareness and planning are vital to the success of any company involved in product design. There are many factors to be considered, all of which are interdependent. When considering economics in product design, think about **resources**. How are they best used, managed and utilised to give greatest efficiency and maximum profits? Listed below are some of the areas which require careful consideration when designing a product for commercial sale:

- Do additional machines and plant have to be bought in order to manufacture the product?
- Will additional training have to be given in order to manufacture the product?
- How long will the product take to manufacture and will this increase the company's wage bill?
- What are the estimated sales for the product and is the market research which estimated this reliable?
- Are the materials to be used to make the product available and affordable?
- Will any of the work need to be subcontracted?
- Can the product be distributed to all the sales outlets quickly and reliably without damaging it?

Other Considerations

The above list is only a sample of the things that have to be considered during the designing of any product. For example, it may be that a proposed design will have to be changed because of difficulties in transporting it. The cost of additional packaging to protect the product in transit may prove to be too high.

Designers and manufacturers can learn valuable lessons by examining other products' successes and failures in the market. Taking the time to explore why some products have proved to be unsuccessful can prevent the same thing happening to them.

Why Products Fail

- Market research may not have been accurate and the estimated sales may have been too high.

- Consumers may decide that the product does not perform as well as they thought or that it has been poorly designed.

- The product is no better than others already on the market and struggles to compete.

- The product may have been wrongly priced. This could mean that the product has been priced too high or too low.

- Advertising and marketing may have been poor and consumers either don't know about the product or have been put off it.

- The product has been beaten to the marketplace by a competitor.

The risks in developing a new product are huge and many companies cannot take the chance of their product failing. Instead they often opt to modify their existing products. Sometimes this means nothing more than just giving the product a 'facelift'. Any innovation or new idea is likely to be copied so quickly by other manufacturers that the product's advantages over its competitors are likely to be short-lived.

From the very beginning of the design process designers must consider the economics of the new product that they are designing. Many of these considerations are listed at the start of this topic.

Designs will change because of aesthetic and functional reasons. However designers must consider the economic effects of this change and the risks involved.

Revise as you go!

- *Give three reasons why a product may prove not to be a commercial success.*

Functional Considerations

Products have many functions, both practical and psychological. Indeed, users may find more functions for a product than the designer originally intended. On the other hand, designers should have a clear idea of what functions they want the product to perform, and whether these are **primary functions** or **secondary functions**.

The primary function of a desk clock may be to display the correct time. This will be a function that the designer will give priority to during the early stages of designing. However, in order for the finished product to function well as a desk clock, the designer will also have to give consideration to other factors. These include stability, weight, centre of gravity, use of materials that will not damage desktops, access for changing batteries, height and angle of the clock to allow a clear view, durability, strength and robustness.

Each of these factors will influence other areas, such as aesthetics and manufacturing, as well as production costs.

Every product will have numerous factors that must be considered to allow it to function and perform efficiently, safely and within laid-down guidelines and standards. Designers must be thorough in their model-making, prototyping and testing to ensure that their products are easy to use, are safe and meet consumer expectations and requirements.

By focusing only on the functional parts of the product it is possible to design something that is ugly and very expensive to manufacture. There has got to be a balance.

Look carefully at a fifth year pupil's first proposal for a mobile phone/minidisk player intended as a fashion accessory for snowboarders and skiers. Up to this point the pupil has only really focused on the functional aspects that deal with how the product will perform. Little thought has been given to other functional concerns and very little given to aesthetics or production requirements.

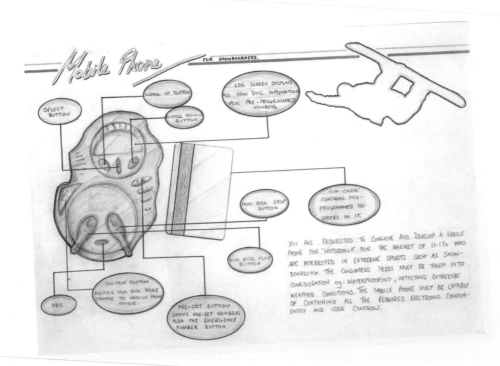

Here is a list of just some of the points that the pupil's teacher made during discussions about the proposal.

■ No consideration has been given to the thickness or profile of this design. You have only thought about it in two dimensions.

■ How is it to be manufactured? What restrictions will this method of manufacture impose on your design?

■ How many separate parts will your product have?

■ Why is the outline shape of the product so 'wavy' and 'wobbly'? Avoid this unless it offers a real benefit to the user. The profile will not make it easier to hold as you suggest. Aesthetically, it looks awkward and clumsy.

■ SIM cards today are much smaller. You are using obsolete technology. You must investigate this area further.

■ The screen could be bigger. It will be difficult to read from it in extreme conditions.

■ The buttons look too small. Remember the user is likely to be wearing gloves.

■ What specification do you require for the material? Impact resistance must be a priority.

■ Is there a headphone socket?

■ The 'open' button requires some thought. Consider its location, its size and what else other than a button could be used to open the CD cover.

These are only some of the points made during discussion. They all relate to function in some way but they also influence the product's appearance and consumer appeal as well as the costs involved in production. Clearly the pupil has a lot of research and development work still to do. Other functional requirements such as ergonomics, material selection and production requirements need to be investigated – as well as getting more familiar with current technology for SIM cards!!

Revise as you go!
- *Explain the difference between a 'primary function' and a 'secondary function'.*
- *Describe three things that must be considered to ensure that the design for an angle poised lamp functions properly.*

Environmental Considerations

Every new product will have some effect on the environment. Designers must consider carefully the environmental impact of any new product, from the production of its raw materials to its ultimate disposal or recycling. This is commonly referred to as the **'Cradle-to-Grave'** approach.

It is now widely recognised that a cradle-to-grave approach needs to be used to assess the environmental impact of a product at every stage of its life. This needs to begin as early as writing the design brief. The designer is the person responsible for generating ideas and ultimately creating new products. It would seem reasonable to expect them to be responsible for the environmental effects of this new creation.

Ultimately the designer loses control of the product when it is bought so the best chance of influencing its effect on the environment is during the designing stage. It is here that decisions can be made on many important environmental issues.

Environmental Decisions at the Design Development Stage

- Look for ways to extend the product's life.

  Products should be fit for their purpose and robust enough to function in their intended environment.

- Do not consciously build in obsolescence

  Wherever possible include a means of upgrading or updating the existing product without it being completely replaced.

- Design products with a minimum number of parts

  This is an obvious way to save resources. Consider miniaturisation and simplification, by avoiding unnecessary decorative parts, for example.

- Design the product for recyclability

  Reduce the number of different materials used in one product. This will make it easier to collect and prepare for recycling at the end of its useful life.

- Construct and assemble products that can remanufactured easily

  If the product can be taken apart easily then it could be refurbished or separated for recycling easily.

- Consider the use of alternative energy sources

  Solar power, wind and water power, and rechargeable power sources are becoming more of an option as technology develops.

Clearly a designer's responsibilities stretch far beyond the obvious considerations of function and aesthetics.

Revise as you go!

- *Write down five things a designer could consider during the design development stage that would make a product more environmentally friendly.*

- *Explain how reducing the number of different materials used on a product could help the environment.*

- *Many products are designed for replacement rather than repair. Explain what this means and describe who it affects.*

Environmental Issues at the Later Stages

Most commercially manufactured products use up natural resources, which are often irreplaceable. Even the way raw materials are extracted from the earth can cause serious environmental problems. Production processes create waste, use energy and, in some cases, produce harmful by-products and emissions. After manufacture, products have to be distributed, displayed, bought and used – all of which will have some impact on the environment. Designers must be aware of these issues and make a conscious effort to limit environmental damage at each stage.

Environmental Protection: The Questions to Ask

Designers have very important roles to play in the conservation and protection of the environment. So much is being said about the dangers of global warming and depletion of the ozone layer that much more basic issues about the design of everyday products are overlooked. Perhaps the following questions will provide a starting point for the design and manufacture of future products:

- Can the product be made from renewable materials?
- Are the proposed materials biodegradable?
- Are the proposed materials recyclable?
- Is the product energy-efficient?
- Can natural power sources be used?
- Are the power sources used rechargeable?
- Can the product be easily repaired?
- Have all the types of pollution that the product may give off, including noise, smell and air, been kept to a minimum?
- Have waste and by-products been kept to a minimum during manufacture?

It is unlikely that the answer to all nine questions will be 'yes', but they are all serious issues which designers need to consider fully. This is especially true now that public concern has led to demands for more legislation to control the environmental effects of commercially produced products.

The Baygen radio was developed initially for use in third world communities who have limited or no energy sources. By winding the handle at the back of the radio it will power a specially developed generator inside that gives around 30 minutes' playing time.

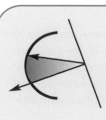

Case Study

Biodegradable materials are gradually being introduced to product design. Visit **www.bpsweb.net** and read about GreenPla. Write down the names of four products that can be made from GreenPla and record this information in your file.

Aesthetic Considerations 1

Why we find certain products attractive and others not so attractive can be very difficult to explain. Even more confusing is why two people looking at the same product can have opposing views on its appearance. Aesthetics therefore should not be considered an exact study. It is not an area in which there are any right or wrong answers. However, trying to understand the basic principles of aesthetics and being able to use them to give an opinion on something will allow us to communicate our thoughts more clearly. We can discuss our view of what is beautiful using the language of aesthetics, but no words will ever make someone see beauty if they themselves do not recognise it. The best we can hope for is that they will understand why we think it is beautiful.

Designers need to understand this. If they know what makes products seem attractive to others then they can use this knowledge to design products which will appeal to others.

Consider the opinions of two pupils who have commented on the visual appearance of the Dyson vacuum cleaner.

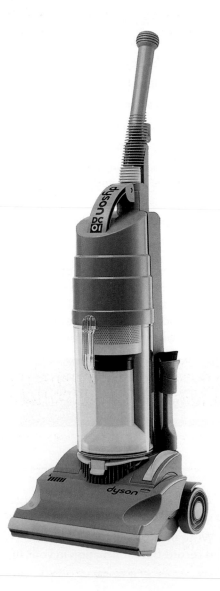

Pupil 1

'I like the appearance of the Dyson vacuum cleaner. It looks technologically advanced and efficient compared to other vacuum cleaners on the market today. It gives the impression that it will do its job well. I feel Dyson has achieved this by choosing a silver grey colour and machine-like forms to give the impression of a well-engineered product. The yellow contrasts well with the grey and draws my attention to the working parts as well as adding interest to the product. I feel the proportion of the yellow to grey is just right.

At first the product looked completely symmetrical but on closer inspection there are subtle differences to each side, which I feel adds interest to it. For example the ribs on the bottom left are balanced visually with the Dyson graphic on the bottom right.

All the main parts of the cleaner visually link together well and have a circular or cylindrical feel to them. The vacuum has a strong image made up from clean uncluttered lines and simple geometric forms.

The clear dust collector allows people to see the cyclonic separator working and is a real focal point for the product whether it is in use or not. This is highlighted further by the strong yellow core which dominates the overall appearance of the product.'

Pupil 2

'I feel the Dyson upright vacuum cleaner looks over-designed and very pretentious. Its overall form appears heavy, bulky and very cumbersome and this is contributed to by the choice of a heavy metal colour. Visually it looks too complicated. For example the handle has lots of rib-like fins which look out of place with the

rest of the product. I would have preferred this part to be smoother and more streamlined. These ribs look unnecessary. The bright yellow colour looks out of place alongside the silver body. I think a colour which harmonises and blends better should have been used. The product has an industrial feel to it and may not appeal to those who wish to use it in their home.'

It is obvious that the two pupils have different opinions about the appearance of the vacuum cleaner. It would be wrong to try to argue that one is right and the other wrong. What is clear is that each can justify their opinion and can comment on the product's aesthetic qualities. Most consumers are not so scientific in their approach. They either like a product or they don't. However designers need to understand why this is so and learn more about why certain products are more aesthetically pleasing than others. This knowledge can then be used to design products that will appeal to the correct market group.

Most people now accept that styling and visual appearance is an important way of adding value to a product without changing its performance. Product styling is about creating visual attractiveness in everyday products.

A product that is attractive will very often grab your attention and appear desirable. Designing a product that is able to do both is a challenge that all product designers are faced with. In addition, consumers are looking for value and originality when they buy a new product.

© Christie's Images/CORBIS

'Lotus' lamp by Louis C Tiffany, USA, c.1900

'Oceanic' lamp by Michele Delucchi

Bigger Picture

These desk lamps were designed eighty years apart and represent the style of their times. The Tiffany lamp, decorative and ornate, represents the Arts and Crafts movement. It was hand crafted using traditional materials and manufacturing processes. The Oceanic is made from more modern material such as plastic laminate and metal with a coloured lacquered finish. The lamp shows simple geometric forms, bright colours and clean lines easily manufactured by machines representative of the Memphis group and post-modern design.

Aesthetic Considerations 2

There was a time when products were hand crafted and the only cost involved was the materials used and the time taken by the craftsman to make the product. In order to add value to these products craftsmen would spend a long time decorating them with ornate features making them more expensive to produce. This would make them more expensive to buy and so add value to them. Today complex forms and ornate decoration can be manufactured for the mass market relatively inexpensively using advanced manufacturing systems. This has caused products with visual complexity to lose some of their prestige value.

Aesthetics covers a range of factors, which affect each other. For example, a **shape** is made up of **lines**. Every shape has a **proportion** and could be described as being **balanced**, **symmetrical**, **dynamic** or **static** in appearance. These words help us to communicate information about shapes and in turn help us examine our feelings towards them.

Every product has numerous aesthetic qualities, which can be examined in depth. They are all linked in some way and are present in every product.

Consider the following:

◆ Shape	◆ Line	◆ Form
◆ Colour	◆ Proportion	◆ Contrast
◆ Pattern	◆ Light	

These are familiar terms and most of us could use them to comment on certain aspects of product design. There are less familiar terms such as harmony, rhythm, unity and balance, which can also be used to express feelings and opinions about a product.

A confident working knowledge of aesthetics will take time to develop. Every designer will become used to making and justifying design decisions which involve the aesthetics of the products they are designing. They will understand how aesthetics can affect people and will become sympathetic towards the tastes, cultures and styles of different market groups.

What Makes a Product Attractive?

There are two distinct stages that we all go through when we examine a product for the first time. At first we simply scan the image quickly looking for patterns, colours, shapes and features. This first stage is vital. If the product doesn't grab our attention quickly or we can find no striking features that have immediate appeal then we are unlikely to be sufficiently interested to go to the second stage. During this second stage we begin to focus on component parts and examine them in detail, trying to gain a deeper understanding of the product. Our brain begins to look for features and images that it understands and is familiar with, while trying to make sense and give some order to features that are new and unfamiliar. Products that have too simple a visual form can seem boring and unattractive. The ideal mix would appear to be a combination of familiar and unfamiliar features within the same product.

People can find products attractive for a variety of reasons. Usually it will have something to do with one of these four scenarios. We can refer to them as the four reasons people find products attractive:

- They have seen a product like it before which they liked, therefore it has a familiar look to it.

- The product looks like it will work well. It looks suited to its purpose and they can understand how to use it.

- The product says something about them. It reflects their style and personality and the image they want to project about themselves.

- They are not sure why they like it. It simply has something about it that has inherent beauty. They probably can't understand why anyone would not find it attractive.

Revise as you go!

- *Do you agree with the statement, 'form follows function'? Choose one product that will back up your view.*

- *Describe how colour can influence a consumer's decision to buy a product.*

Ergonomics 1

Have you ever sat in a chair and found it uncomfortable? Have you experienced having to pull or push a door a few times before you were able to open it? Have you seen someone grapple with a jar because the lid won't open? Products can frustrate us. They will cause inconvenience, anxiety and occasionally injury if they have not been designed with the user in mind. Well-designed products are easy to use and we often become attracted to the efficiency of how they work. This attraction extends beyond aesthetics and is not concerned with visual beauty. The attraction lies in how the product interacts with us and the effect it has on our way of life.

Usually the first interaction we have with a product is through sight. We will look at it and very quickly make a judgement on how the product should be used, which parts should be touched and if there are any safety issues. These initial observations can lead to snap judgements being made. We may say things like, 'That doesn't look safe', or 'That product looks difficult to use'. These are things which clearly cannot be fully established until the product has been tried and tested but the process of human interaction has begun.

Our next interaction is often through touch. As we begin to examine the product more closely we will want to press buttons, open covers or lids and feel its surface texture. This process of 'checking things out' can stimulate enough interest for us to try out the product for real. We may sit in the chair, lie on the bed, listen to the CD player, pick up the camera and look through the lens. When we experience these things the product begins to give us feedback. These first impressions are important and may lead to a more informed opinion about the product's capabilities. Successful products work well because they satisfy a number of human requirements as well as enabling the user to interact with it easily and efficiently.

Ergonomics: A Definition

Ergonomics is the study of how humans interact with their environments and the products in them. It seeks to achieve the most advantageous matches between **products, environments and systems** and the **capacities, needs and inclinations** of the people who use them. 'Ergonomics' is synonymous with **human factors**. The term is derived from two Greek words: 'ergon' (work or task) and 'nomos' (a law or rule). There are two main principles for consideration: fitting the person to the activity and fitting the activity to the person. Ergonomics is also known as 'human engineering', that is design with regard to human bodies.

Ergonomics has three areas for consideration:

(i) Anthropometrics

This is the study of the measurements and dimensions of the human body. We will examine this in more detail later but it is important to realise that the dimensions of any product must have a direct relationship to the dimensions of the user.

(ii) Physiology

An understanding of the human body's capabilities is essential when designing products in order to avoid stress, strain, fatigue and the possibility of injury. Careful consideration must be given to factors as diverse as strength, muscle control, posture, flexibility, joint movement and reaction times.

(iii) Psychology

Mental and emotional triggers can stimulate human behaviour. It is important to have an understanding of how people receive, perceive and process information in order to design products which are appealing and easy to use. The products we choose say something about us but the reason we chose them in the first place is because they have appealed to our senses and triggered a favorable response which we often summarise by simply saying, 'I like that'.

The design of any product, system or environment to be used by people should be influenced by ergonomics.

Consider the BMW 3 series to briefly examine how these three areas of ergonomics have been applied to certain parts of the car.

Psychology

The door **feels** and **sounds** solid and robust when it is opened and closed, creating a feeling of safety. The dashboard and controls are well laid out and **look** easy to understand, creating a feeling of efficiency. The **sound** of the engine creates a feeling of a car that has been well engineered and should be reliable. That 'new car **smell**' creates an impression that it is clean, expensive and well looked after. It is easy to see how these things are designed to appeal to our **senses** and create a feeling that this is an expensive product that has been well manufactured and is reliable.

Physiology

Natural body movements can operate all the controls in the car. For example **extending** the leg to press a pedal, **gripping** the hand brake, **flicking** a switch with fingers and **pressing** buttons. These are common to all cars but the shape and the way these controls move are designed to suit the capabilities and constraints of the user's hands, feet and legs so that they can be operated and controlled easily.

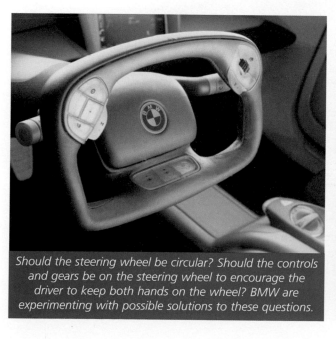

Should the steering wheel be circular? Should the controls and gears be on the steering wheel to encourage the driver to keep both hands on the wheel? BMW are experimenting with possible solutions to these questions.

Car designers are focusing on the need to optimise the driver's condition, e.g. car entertainment controls, providing an easy reach for the steering wheel.

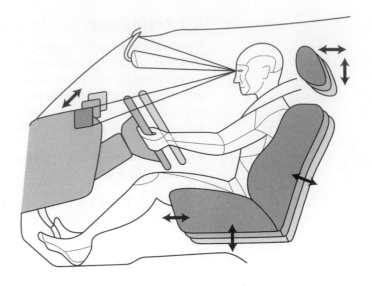

Anthropometrics

There are three things to consider here. **Reach**, **clearance** and **posture**. Reach would be based on the 5th percentile of the population (smallest); an example of this would be the positioning of the controls so as they can be easily reached. Clearance would be based on the 95th (tallest). Consider the headroom when seated and the legroom beneath the steering wheel. Best postural positioning is achieved through adjustability to the seat to allow comfortable driving for a range of people.

Revise as you go!

- *What ergonomic factors must be considered in the design of a domestic iron?*
- *Explain the difference between anthropometrics and ergonomics.*
- *Give four examples of products where the physiological constraints of the user have been of prime importance.*

Case Study

Ergonomics is a vital consideration when designing products for use by humans. Visit The Design Council website at **www.designcouncil.org.uk** to see examples of how ergonomics has been used in the design of recent products. Make notes and add them to your file.

Ergonomic Factors in Design Planning

When using ergonomic factors in design planning for any product it may be useful to consider the following:

- The purpose of the product and its operating conditions
- Human posture and body position (standing, sitting, reclining), allowing for movement
- Physical dimensions and space, allowing for things such as clothing, access and movement
- The future maintenance of the product
- The use of adjustable equipment to improve operating conditions.

Other areas to consider include the following:

- For fast and efficient use, controls and indicators should be grouped and positioned within the normal cone of vision. Fatigue can be minimised by careful grouping and positioning.
- Precise control and improved operating conditions may require good body or limb support.
- The pressure or force used will depend on the amount of leverage, body position and weight.
- Trials and tests should be carried out on people who range between the 5th and 95th percentiles (*see* **Anthropometrics**). Scale models or full-scale mock-ups can be used.
- The limiting factors of the design should be examined.

Bigger Picture

Shopping for electrical goods often results in pressing buttons and switches just to see what happens. How often have we pressed the eject button on a CD player in a shop? How the product reacts once the button has been pressed creates an immediate impression on us. How did the button feel? What signals did it give us to say that it had been pressed? Was it a visual signal or a sound? Did we feel any resistance, click or vibration? Even the location of the button, its size and shape have a lot to do with the human interaction required to make a product successful.

Anthropometrics

People come in many shapes and sizes. Anthropometrics is the branch of ergonomics which deals with the measurement of the physical characteristics of human beings. The range of body sizes varies from one country to another and, with improved nutrition, from one generation to the next. The designer's goal is to cater for as wide a range of people as possible (the target population).

Every product must interact in some way with people at some stage in its life. So when designing products it makes sense to use the measurements of the people who are to use them as the basis for the products' dimensions.

Products should be designed around the **dimensions**, **capabilities** and **responses** of the people who will use them. This information is available from many sources. There are numerous publications available which provide data for almost every part of the human body for a variety of age groups. This data will include everything from the standing height of a fully-grown adult to the length of the index finger of a toddler. Finding these sizes and getting access to the required data should not be a problem for any designer willing to look for it. However knowing how to use it is something that has to be thought about and considered carefully.

There is no point designing for the average person. By doing this products will prove to be unsuitable for the majority of people who will use them. A very simple and obvious example of this is the height of a door in a house. The average height of a fully-grown adult will be around 174 centimetres and if doors were this height then 50% of the people who walked through them would have to bend down to avoid hitting their head. Instead door sizes are bigger, taking account of a wider range of people and providing them with some clearance room for things like hats. Still a few people will have difficulty getting through doors. This is an important observation as it would be impossible to design a product that suits everyone. The world's tallest man was measured at 2.72 metres. Clearly it would be impossible and unnecessary to design every doorway to accommodate him.

The 5th– 95th Percentile

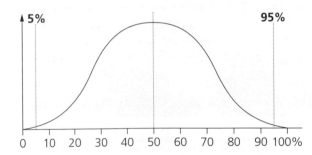

We are all individuals and our body sizes are all different. The graph shows the normal distribution curve for a given number of people against height. Some people are tall, others are short but the majority of us fall within the 5% to 95% region shown on the graph. This graph can be repeated for every body part and designers need to decide if they are to select a size that relates to the 5th percentile or one that relates to the 95th. This is best illustrated in seating design.

An ergonome has been drawn (top of next page) in a seated position to represent someone sitting typing at a computer terminal. Size D represents the popliteal height, which is based on the length of a person's leg from a point behind the knee to the bottom of the foot. For comfort it would be best to have the foot flat on the floor therefore the 5th percentile size should be used. If the 50th or 95th were used then many people would be left in the uncomfortable position of having their legs left dangling in mid-air. For best results it is desirable to design products that are adjustable, allowing people to set them to their own individual requirements. This is a

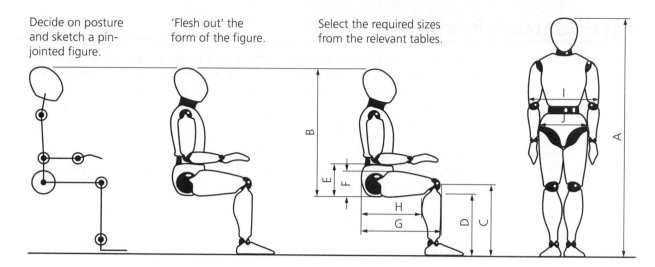

Decide on posture and sketch a pin-jointed figure.

'Flesh out' the form of the figure.

Select the required sizes from the relevant tables.

Body Feature	Male, Percentile		
	5th	50th	95th
A Stature	1625	1740	1855
B Sitting height	850	910	970
C Knee height, sitting	495	540	590
D Popliteal height	400	440	480
E Elbow rest height	190	240	285
F Thigh clearance	125	150	175
G Buttock-knee length	540	595	645
H Buttock-popliteal length	440	495	550
I Forearm to forearm	390	450	510
J Hip breadth	315	360	400
K Weight (lbs)	145	181	217

(all sizes in millimetres)

much more expensive process and is an option that is not always possible for every product in every situation.

The aim is to target 90% of the population. 5% at either end of the scale are outwith this range. These limits are known as the 5th and 95th percentiles. You can find these measurements in anthropometric tables, which contain vast amounts of information on human dimensions.

If we were to consider car seating, then, the position of the figure would be quite different. Driving is an activity that requires movement therefore decisions need to be taken about clearance between head and roof and easy reach to pedals, steering wheel and dashboard controls, as well as **posture** for maximum comfort. Initial decisions can be based on using the 95th percentile for **clearance** and the 5th percentile for **reach**. This is known as the 'method of limits'.

Sitting is actually a dynamic activity and this becomes obvious when we experience aches and pains as a result of remaining in the same position for a prolonged period of time. Accurate static anthropometric data provide a reliable starting point but consideration must be given to cushioning, arm and head supports as well as clearance from other surrounding products.

The **50th percentile** size is rarely used but in certain situations involving hand sizes it is the most appropriate.

Other more specific areas of anthropometric data available to designers include **noise levels** and **light levels** for different situations as well as **strength requirements** for people having to lift, squeeze, push and pull products.

Revise as you go!

- *Use products with which you are familiar to explain the 5th and 95th percentile.*
- *Give an example of where the 50th percentile would be used.*

Intellectual Property

Anyone who has lost something or had any of their personal belongings stolen will know how awful they can feel. Can you imagine how it must feel to have invented something new only to have someone steal your idea, use it before you, and pretend that it was theirs?

This has been a problem for product designers for centuries. One well-known example was Alexander Graham Bell and Elisha Gray, who both claimed the patent to the telephone back in 1876! Bell has been given the credit for it because he registered the idea before Gray but there is still some debate as to who actually came up with the idea first.

Protecting Intellectual Property

The issue of protecting thoughts and ideas is a complex one, especially for product designers. Take for example the jug kettle found in most homes and high street stores today. Up until the late 1970s kettles did not look like this. Instead the handle went over the lid, they had no water level indicators and most were made from metal. A typical example was the Russell Hobbs kettle shown opposite. Whoever came up with the idea of using plastic for the main body, including a water level indicator enabling it to be filled through the spout, putting the handle on the side and making it cordless has clearly produced a safer product which is far easier to use. This idea should be a market leader and the company that first produced it should have little or no competition in the high street. However, nearly all new kettles have these improved features and are very similar in how they perform. Competition between companies has become fierce in a marketplace which has reached saturation point.

So protecting good ideas and keeping them a secret from your competitors is very difficult especially when anyone can have access to the idea through buying the product. New products have an obvious commercial value and they are the **intellectual property** of the designer. This intellectual property must also have a value and needs to be protected.

There are now five ways of formally protecting an idea or a design:

■   Registering a **trade mark**

This allows a company to protect the name and identity of their product. It prevents anyone else using someone else's name to sell their own product. For example if we buy a Nike T-shirt we can be assured that it is a Nike product provided it displays the Nike graphic. If another company wishes to trade under the Nike name they must first buy the trademark. One of the most expensive trademarks to be bought by another company is Kit-Kat. Nestle, bought this name from Rowntree MacIntosh some years ago and now manufacture and sell the product themselves keeping the same name and image for the chocolate bar. A trademark is recognised by the symbol ®.

■   Holding the **copyright**

This is mainly used on printed and published materials. The copyright normally belongs

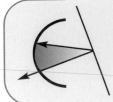

Case Study

Find three examples of legal cases that involve a dispute over intellectual property. Visit **www.design-council.org.uk** and record these examples in your file.

Russell Hobbs K2 kettle designed in 1959.

Russell Hobbs Millennium kettle designed in 1996.

to the author or the originator of a work, but the publisher or company responsible for producing the material can own the copyright if that has been agreed. Indeed anyone can own the copyright to a piece of work if they have a written agreement from the person who originated the material. Proving copyright can be done easily. First a copyright symbol © needs to be put on the work and then it should be placed in a sealed envelope and posted back to the author. Provided the envelope remains unopened and it has a postmark on it confirming the date, then copyright has been proved.

- **Registering** the design

This is a method of protecting the appearance of a product but it is seldom enough to protect how the product functions and works. The process is administered through the patents office and a fee is required annually to keep a product registered in a company's name. Once a product has been designed it should be taken to the patents office where they will carry out a search to establish if the same, or a similar product has previously been registered. If they are satisfied that this has not happened then they will grant registration.

- Establishing a **design right**

This is a very similar process to establishing a copyright but in this case it is appropriate to 3-dimensional products. The designer should photograph the product, sign and date the photograph and write on it 'Design Right' before placing it into a sealed envelope and posting it to themselves. From there the process works in the same way as copyright.

- Being granted a **patent**.

The facility to grant a patent has been with us for over 500 years. There are millions of products all over the world that have been granted a patent. For this to be granted the product must have a feature that makes it different from any other similar product type. It is also a requirement that the product has not been shown in public before. When a patent has been granted it gives the owner a licence to make money from the product with the security that it cannot be copied for up to twenty years. Anyone who has an invention or has discovered a new method of doing an established task needs to patent the idea, otherwise other commercial design companies will use the idea to develop their own products.

Kettle design has come a long way since the K2. Improved features of the Millennium kettle include the position of the handle, a flat disc element which boils water much quicker and cuts down on limescale, a body made from polypropylene, and a water level indicator. This feature has been made possible through developments in injection moulding allowing two different materials to be injected simultaneously before fusing together inside the mould. This is called two shot moulding. The kettle is cordless, lightweight and can boil small amounts of water.

Revise as you go!
- *What do you understand by the term 'intellectual property'?*
- *What are the main criteria for a product to be granted a patent?*
- *Describe how a designer can copyright their material without showing it to anyone else.*

SECTION 3
Practice

Section 3: Practice

Design for Manufacture

To be a success in the marketplace products must have certain attributes. It is essential that the designer ensures that:

- the product functions as intended
- the product looks good and is considered desirable
- the product is cost effective
- the product is able to be manufactured.

It is unlikely that for a commercially produced product complete responsibility for all of these things will be given to one person. A team approach is more likely and is in accordance with concurrent engineering methods. Members of the design and production team are aware of the demands of manufacturing and the relative costs involved. This teamwork approach means that efficient cost-effective decisions can be made and necessary changes to both the design and the manufacture of a product can be discussed at an early stage.

Standardisation

Standard components, materials and production procedures all have to be costed and planned prior to the start of manufacture. Standardisation of these things will cut costs and this is particularly true if it can be applied to more than one product at a time. The motor car is a good example of this approach. Some parts can be used across a range of cars and can even be used in partnership with other manufacturers. For example Volkswagen, Audi, Seat and Skoda all share parts in their various models.

Modern Manufacturing Methods

An understanding of how things are manufactured in an industrial context is vital to the successful outcome of bringing a new product to the marketplace.

Modern manufacturing methods offer great flexibility and variety of choice to designers. Complex curvilinear shapes and forms are much easier to manufacture than ever before. Surface textures and small detail are becoming common practice as methods of mould making embrace new technology and production methods. However, there are still restrictions to the common working practices that designers must observe in the design of any mass-produced product. A close examination of an everyday product will reveal certain similarities. A few of the design features relating to plastic casings are outlined in the following list:

- **Split lines**

  These occur naturally when two parts of the outside casing of a product join together. One part of the casing will locate inside the other part, often leaving a

Revise as you go!
- *Explain why standard components are so important to manufacturers.*
- *Why are webs used in the design of plastic casings for products?*

small groove running along the length of the product. Split lines are usually found at the widest part of a product.

- **Break lines**

    These appear as lines or grooves on the surfaces of parts of a product. They are used to divide up otherwise featureless areas or to add details or features to one part of the product. On large flat surfaces, break lines can be used to disguise distortions that may appear as a result of manufacturing.

- **Tapered sides**

    These are necessary parts of any components that have to be injection moulded. The tapered sides allow these parts to be easily removed from moulds. Tapers are often as little as 1°.

- **Radius corners**

    These allow molten plastic to flow easily around moulds. They strengthen corners and allow for parts to be easily removed from moulds.

- **Webs**

    These are usually internal features which are used to add strength or support to parts. On some products, webs are visible on the outside and so can be used as a feature.

- **Surface textures**

    Textures or patterns can be used on the surface of any mass-produced product. They are produced by a process called spark erosion, which is a method of texturing the inside surface of moulds.

Other considerations include the location of injection and ejection points (which appear as small blemishes on the surface of products). They are usually designed to be hidden on parts that are not easily seen or are not normally looked at.

When designing for manufacture it makes good sense to examine and analyse how other products that use similar manufacturing processes are made.

The battery cover for a remote control has been removed. From the picture it is clear to see internal webs, tapered sides and radiused corners on the cover. Break lines and split lines are visible on the remote.

Choosing a Material

There are so many different materials available for the production of products that selecting the most appropriate can be a time-consuming task. To avoid problems such as material failure it is worth adopting a systematic approach to identifying the most appropriate one for any product. There are a large number of considerations here, including functional requirements, manufacturing restrictions, and the availability and cost of the materials.

Properties

The prime consideration in all of this is understanding the properties of the materials that are available for selection. The following properties are identified as being important factors in determining the suitability of a particular material for a product or part of a product:

- **Mechanical**   the ability to resist and support a force
- **Physical**   size, density and surface texture should be considered
- **Thermal**   the ability to withstand temperature change
- **Chemical**   how a material reacts to corrosion and chemicals
- **Electrical**   how a material conducts or resists electrical currents
- **Optical**   the abilities to transmit and refract light
- **Acoustical**   the abilities to absorb and transfer sound.

Mechanical properties that should be considered are:

- **Strength**   the ability of the material to resist either tensile, compressive or shear force
- **Toughness**   a measure of the energy a material can absorb before fracture: a material that is not tough is brittle
- **Hardness**   the ability to resist scratching, abrasion and wear
- **Stiffness**   the ability of a material to deform temporarily under force then return to its original shape when the force is removed (elasticity)
- **Ductility**   the ability of a material to be deformed permanently by stretching, bending or twisting: ductile materials must be strong as well as malleable
- **Malleability**   the ability of a material to be permanently deformed in all directions without rupture.

Designers are also concerned with aesthetic qualities such as colour, texture, shape and ability to reflect light.

Testing a Material

Choosing a material for the production of a product may require the examination and testing of materials used in other products. This can be done in simulated conditions and is a useful way of finding out how the material will perform in its expected environment. Testing can answer questions such as:

Is the material suited to the expected tasks it is likely to perform?

Does it meet the specification for the new product?

How will sunlight and other external elements affect the material?

These are important questions that need accurate and reliable answers, which can only be given once testing is complete.

Cost Implications

Once a suitable material has been decided upon then its cost implications have to be assessed. As always, keeping costs down is a necessary part of the process and there may be substitute materials that will perform just as efficiently. In deciding this the questions to be asked could follow a similar format to those below:

What is the material?

What properties does it possess?

What does it cost?

What other material could do the same job?

How much will that cost?

This analytical approach to choosing a material is called **Value Engineering**. The principal objective here is to find ways in which a particular function can be achieved at reduced cost by substituting an alternative material.

The Systematic Approach

If material failure is to be avoided it is best to adopt a systematic approach to the selection of any material. There are many things to consider and a list of headings of some of the relevant factors to aid with materials selection is provided below. Each one of these headings should generate much discussion, testing and research work.

Choosing materials depends on:

- properties
- costs
- available resources
- number to be produced
- product complexity
- effect on the environment
- design requirements
- social factors
- service requirements.

Revise as you go!

- *Why is it important to consider the functional requirements of a product before deciding on a material?*
- *What properties must a material have to make it suitable for use in a children's play park?*
- *What impact have new materials had on the design of products in the last ten years?*

Plastics

The basic chemicals used in the manufacture of plastics are extracted from coal and crude oil. These are obtained by using heat and chemical catalysts. There are four main stages in converting these raw materials into plastic products:

- Extraction of the basic chemicals from **crude oil**
- Refining and processing the basic chemicals into **monomers**
- Converting the refined chemicals into **polymers** in the form of plastic granules
- Processing the plastic granules into **products**.

Additives can be used to modify the properties of the plastic depending on what the product will be.

Fillers such as powdered chalk can be used to bulk out the plastic changing its appearance and reducing cost.

Pigments can be added to give the plastic colour.

Additives such as carbon fibres can be used to improve the strength of the material.

Stabilisers are used to guard against decomposition or damage caused by light.

Flame retardants reduce the flammability of commonly used plastics.

Lubricants help the flow of the plastic during processing.

Blowing agents release gas to make foamed or expanded plastics.

Plastics were initially used as a substitute for more expensive materials. An example of this was a semi-synthetic material called parkesine being used to replace the natural ivory used to make billiard balls. Other early plastic products included jewellery, knife handles, combs, pens and toys. These products acquired the reputation of being cheap.

The idea of plastic being an imitation of the real thing has taken a long time to eradicate. This notion is now fading with the recognition that only plastic materials possess some of the vital properties and characteristics that are suited to new technology. Plastics are now strongly associated with the products we use today and will undoubtedly be an increasing functional element of the products of the future. Psychologically there is now an unquestioning acceptance of the match between high technology products and the use of plastic materials.

The wide range of plastics now available are natural or synthetic resins or compounds that can be moulded, extruded, cast or used as thin film or coatings. New plastics are now being introduced almost continuously. Their uses and applications are expanding and are replacing many traditional wood and metal materials in product design. The composition of the plastic can be altered to suit specific product requirements and specifications by including additives, pigments, fillers, stabilisers and lubricants.

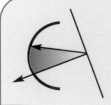

Case Study

The Universale Chair was designed by Joe Colombo in 1965 but it took a further two years before it was ready for mass production. Visit the Design Museum website at **www.designmuseum.org/** to find out more about Joe Colombo. Print a picture of the Universale Chair and add it to your file. Which plastic was the chair made from? Find another two products made by Colombo and add these to your file.

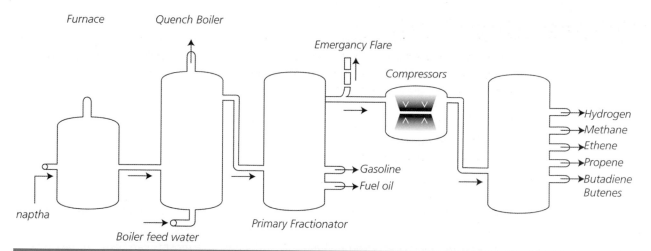

*Crude oil first undergoes fractional distillation.
Further alterations using a cracking plant are required before the plastic can be used for manufacture.*

Plastics are ideal for mass production of quality products, and can duplicate or better the properties of most other materials, including aluminium, glass, rubber and steel.

Properties

General properties include:

- light weight
- resistance to corrosion
- low thermal conductivity
- can be translucent, transparent and opaque
- electrically resistant
- easily formed
- recyclable.

Forms

Plastics can also be supplied in various forms:

- profiled sheets, rods, tubes and bars
- moulding compounds
- thin layers of films and sheets
- foam
- casting compounds such as ingots
- paint, varnish and lacquer used for finishing
- filaments and fibres
- composites which contain reinforcing material.

Revise as you go!

- *Identify four qualities which plastics offer a product designer over traditional materials such as wood and metal.*
- *Name two additives that can be used with plastics. Explain the purpose of using each additive.*

Thermosetting Plastics

These plastics are formed by chemical reactions which leave them in a relatively fixed state. Thermosetting plastics are formed and 'set' in a single operation when a chemical reaction leaves them 'fixed' in the shape of the mould. They cannot be softened or reformed when reheated. This irreversible condition is normally induced by an activator with a base resin at the time of moulding or reforming the plastic into its final shape. Although thermosets can withstand high temperatures, excess heat will simply cause the material to decompose.

An egg yolk is a good analogy for this. When a yolk is raw, it is in a soft liquid state. But if it is heated, it becomes hard and is no longer capable of becoming soft.

Thermosetting plastics are often used when a product needs resistance to extremes in temperature, electrical current, chemicals and wear. Thermosets can resist impact when reinforced, an example being Glass Reinforced Plastic (GRP).

Name	Common name	Properties and working characteristics	Uses
Epoxy resin (ER)	Araldite	excellent adhesive qualities, low shrinkage, strong when reinforced	bonding, encapsulation, laminating, surface coating
Melamine formaldehyde (MF)	Formica Melaware	waterproof, tasteless, odourless, mark and scratch resistant	worktops, tableware, buttons, electrical insulation, e.g. in distributor caps
Urea formaldehyde (UF)	Aerolyte Cascamite	good adhesive qualities, stiff, hard, brittle, good electrical insulator	electrical fittings, paper and textile coating, wood adhesive
Polyester resin (PR)	Orel Beetle	stiff, hard, brittle, resilient as laminated GRP, formed without heat or pressure	panels for car bodies and boat hulls, casting, embedding

Revise as you go!
- *Name three thermosetting plastics.*
- *List four products that have been made from thermosetting plastics. Name the manufacturing processes used to produce them.*

The Memphis group designed for mass production. They deliberately used colourful patterned plastic laminates, such as melamine and formica, to transform drab boards into desirable pieces of furniture.

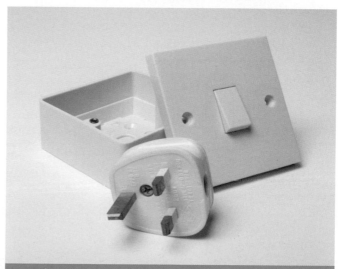

Electrical fittings are today compression moulded in thermosetting plastics. This gives them good insulation properties as well as a much higher melting point than thermo-plastics.

Thermoplastics

Thermoplastics soften when heated and harden again when cooled. This softening and hardening can be repeated indefinitely. Ice is a good analogy for this. When it is cold, it is hard and cannot be moulded. When it is heated, it returns to a liquid state and can be poured easily.

When thermoplastics are soft, they are easily formed under pressure. When gently reheated, a thermoplastic will return to its original shape. This is called plastic memory. Thermoplastics are used in products which do not have to withstand high temperatures. The particular plastic chosen for a given application will depend on the product specification and the intended use.

Name	Common name	Properties and working characteristics	Uses
Polyethene (HDPE)	Polythene (old name: Polyethylene)	High Density: tough, resists chemicals, feels waxy	rigid: buckets, bowls, sterlisied containers
(LDPE)		Low denisty: soft and pliable, electric insulator	flexible: bags, bottles, cable sheathing, toys
Polypropene (PP)	Propathene (old name: Polypropylene)	rigid, light, good chemical resistance, resistance to fatigue, bending	crates, seats, string, rope, medical equipment, hinges, kitchenware, film
Polystyrene (PS)		light, buoyant, stiff, water resistant	packaging, containers, insulation, toys
Polyvinyl chloride (uPVC)		rigid, abrasive resistance, water/weather resistent	pipes, gutters, bottles, roofing, window frames
(plasticised)		soft flexible, electrical insulator	wire insulation, wall covering, hosepipes
Poly-methacrylate (PMMA)	Acrylic Perspex	stiff, hard, clear, durable, scratches easily, easily machined and polished	signs, lighting, reflectors/lenses, cases, jewellery
Polyamide (PA)	Nylon	tough, durable, machines well, self-lubricating	bearings, gears, bristles, textiles, clothing, upholstery
Acrylonitrile butadiene styrene (ABS)		strong, light, duarble, scratch/chemical resistent, high surface finish	kitchenware, toys, cases, crash helmets, telephones
Cellulose acetate		hard, tough, can be made flexible, light, transparent	photo film, packaging, lids, containers

Elastomers

Elastomers are a particular branch of thermoplastics which, as the name suggests, have elastic properties. They can be likened to rubber in how they react to pressure and in how they feel to the touch. Elastomers can withstand a particularly large amount of deformation and many can be stretched to several times their original length.

Uses of elastomers range from waterproof seals and diaphragms used for mechanical purposes, to flexible handles, sportswear and foam padding.

Bigger Picture

A Danish carpenter named Godtfred Kirk invented a method of interlocking wooden play blocks. By the 1950s Lego had developed the idea and were manufacturing injection moulded blocks made from thermoplastic. Today Lego is one of the top ten toy manufacturers. It has sold over 320 billion Lego blocks.

Plastic buckets and washbasins are familiar household items. Made from HDPE (High Density polyethylene) they are rigid and able to withstand temperatures beyond the point of boiling water.

Acrylic or perspex is universally used in all kinds of lighting applications and has replaced glass in many cases because of its lightweight impact resistance properties.

Revise as you go!

- *What property of a thermoplastic makes it particularly suitable for injection moulding?*
- *Describe the properties of elastomers.*

Testing Plastics

Today most products which are made from plastic have an identification mark on them. However this may not always be the case. There may also be occasions when plastic parts have not been accurately identified and tests will have to be carried out before these parts can be named. These tests are quite simple and need not involve using expensive or dangerous equipment. The tests can be carried out in the classroom and if done in sequence can be used to identify most plastics.

1. Cut a small sample from the product with a knife. The knife can be heated first to allow easier cutting.

2. Drop the sample onto a hard surface and listen for the sound it makes.

3. Test to see if the sample floats.

4. Examine the surface finish of the plastic.

5. Scratch the surface with a sharp object.

6. Heat the sample gently over a candle.

7. Burn the plastic.

8. Examine the colour of the flame and smoke.

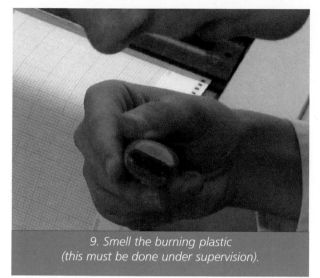

9. Smell the burning plastic (this must be done under supervision).

During each of these nine stages it is important to observe how the plastic reacts and performs. The flow chart below gives an indication of what to look for and how it is possible to begin the process of naming the plastic.

Experience is important, particularly when it comes to identifying a smell and in some cases it may only be possible for you to reduce the possibilities down to a small range. More specialised tests may be required such as carrying out the float test in different densities of water. Salty water for example is much denser and some plastics which sink in normal water may now float. Adding alcohol will make the water less dense and plastics which may have floated in normal water may now sink.

Examining the plastic under a microscope can also help to identify if there are some additives and fillers used.

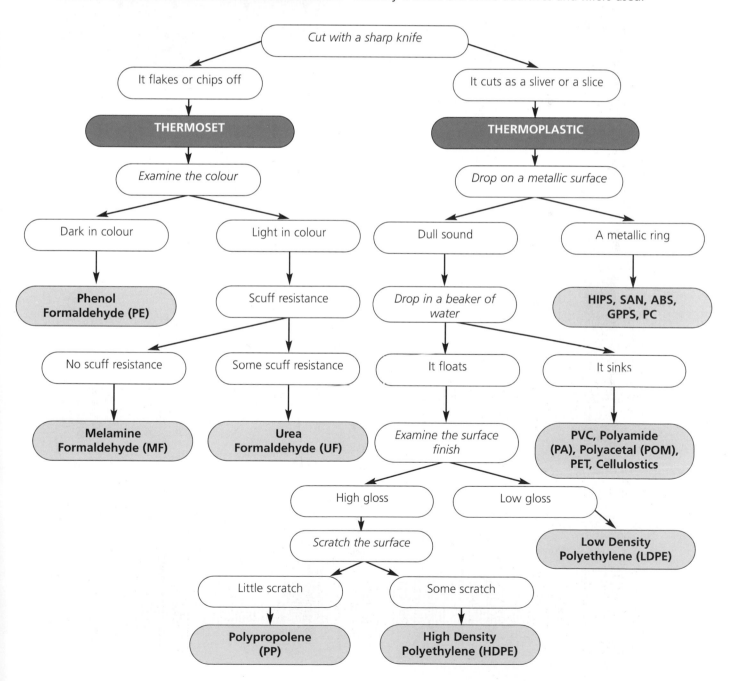

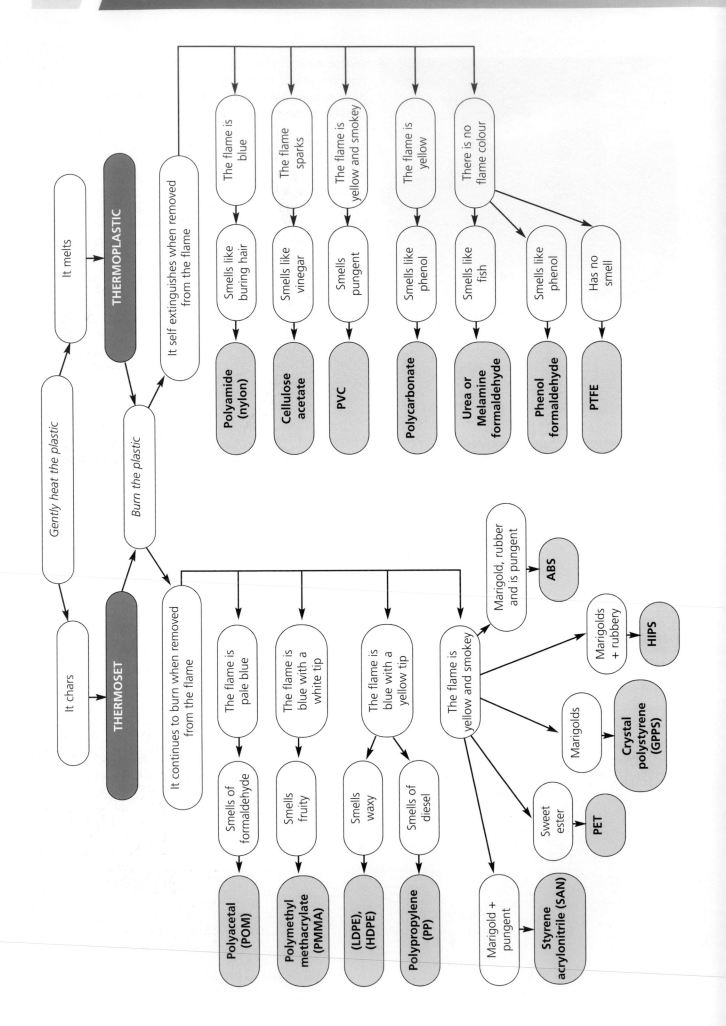

Identifying and Naming Plastics

Recognising and naming plastics can be difficult. As new polymers have been developed, their systematic names, derived from complex chemical formulae, have been reduced to 'trivial' names for easier common usage. Capital letters, abbreviations and trade names can be used. Examples of these include PVC, polythene and Teflon.

Coding System

42% of all plastics are used in packaging products and, conveniently, the plastics industry has introduced a coding system which is now in use in Europe, America and Australia. The code means that plastics can easily be identified for recycling purposes.

PET/PETE
polyethane terephthalate

HDPE
high density polyethane

V or PVC
vinyl or polyvinyl chloride

LDPE
low density polyethane

PP
polypropene

PS
polystyrene

Other
including multi-layer

Designers are continually extending the uses of plastics by taking advantage of the benefits they offer while making allowances for their limitations. 26 million tonnes are processed annually in the UK. Industrial applications include construction, packaging, transport and electronics.

The Tribopen

New technology is being developed to identify unmarked plastics. A recent invention is the 'Tribopen'. The Tribopen is a simple hand-held device which has different snap-on heads. The pen works on the principle of measuring an electrostatic charge between different heads and different plastics.

Revise as you go!
- *What does HDPE stand for?*
- *What is the reason for the coding system found on plastic components?*

Composite Materials

A composite material consists of two or more substances which combine to produce properties which cannot be achieved by any of the individual substances.

A good example is the use of carbon fibres embedded in resin (carbon-fibre reinforced plastic or CFRP). CFRP is a composite which is low in density, and therefore light in weight, but has high tensile strength. This composite has better corrosion resistance and fatigue performance than most of the metal alloys it replaces. It is used in the aerospace industry and for car chassis.

One of the components forms the matrix (base material) while the other component provides the reinforcement. The properties of the composite are controlled by the size and distribution of the reinforcing substance.

There are four principal ways to reinforce a composite material:

- **Dispersion composites**

  These contain very fine particles (1 to 15% in volume) which harden the material by preventing the spread of internal defects. SAP (Sintered Aluminium Powder), a composite of alumina in aluminium, is an example of a dispersion composite. A dispersion composite is characterised by increased strength which is unaltered by increases in temperature.

- **Particulate composites**

  These contain larger particles (greater than 20% in volume). The brittle nature of ceramics has resulted in a large number of reinforced materials in this class, e.g. grinding wheels and ceramic-tipped cutting tools.

- **Fibrous composites**

  These come in a wide variety of materials. The parent material is used to bind the fibres together and protect the surface from damage. Fibre reinforced plastics (FRPs) – glass fibres in a polyester resin mix used in boat hulls and car bodies – are examples of fibrous composites.

- **Laminated or Layer Composites**

  These have alternate layers of material bonded together and can consist of thin coatings, thicker protective surfaces, claddings, bi-metallic layers, laminates or sandwiches. Plywood is probably the most common example. Safety glasses have a plastic film sandwiched between two sheets of glass, decorative formica is used in furniture and shop fittings.

Revise as you go!
- *Write down three advantages composite materials have over traditional materials. Give an example of a product for each advantage.*
- *Why are composite materials being used more frequently by designers?*

Metal Matrix Composites

Fibre reinforced metals (FRMs) are being used more frequently because of their improved stiffness, high heat resistance and wear properties. Fibres such as silicon carbide and alumina are used.

Natural Composites

Wood and leather are almost exclusively polymer/fibre composites.

Smart Materials

The properties of materials remain more or less constant. '**Smart**' materials, however, respond to light and temperature. They are used in 'reactolite' sunglasses, for example. Shape memory alloys (SMAs), e.g. Nitinol (made from nickel and titanium), retain their shape until heated. SMAs have high electrical resistance and can be heated by passing an electric current through them. The ability to provide large forces and movement makes SMAs suitable for electrical connectors, triggers and valves.

© Randy Faris/CORBIS

Vaulting poles are made using a carbon fibre composite to provide increased strength, flexibility and elasticity. Composite materials are used extensively in the world of sport.

Tennis rackets are made from a composite of polyamide fibre in epoxy resin.

Plastics Processing

Plastics are usually supplied as moulding powder, granules or chips which have to be processed. Processing includes the thorough mixing of additives with the moulding powder, granules or chips to produce plastic compounds. The use of additives allows a relatively small number of base plastics to be transformed into a wide range of very versatile materials.

Types of Plastic Processing

- **Injection moulding**

  Usually for thermoplastics. Molten plastics are injected under pressure into a mould. The mould surface detail (profile of the product) can be accurately reproduced.

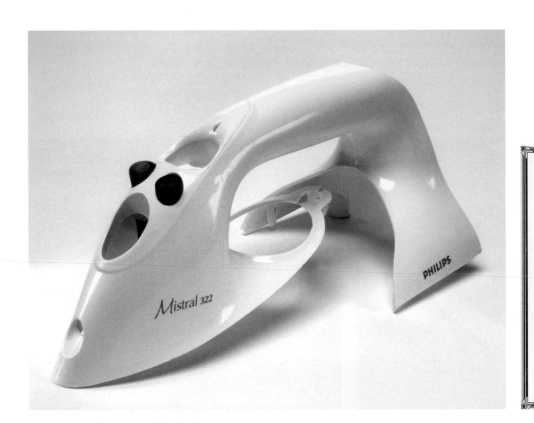

- **Compression moulding**

  Usually for thermosetting plastics. Plastic is moulded under pressure before the polymerisation reaction begins.

- **Extrusion**

  Usually for thermoplastics. The molten plastics are fed under pressure by a screw through a hole or a die. Long continuous lengths, such as sheets, rods and tubes, can be produced.

- **Thermoforming** (vacuum forming)

  Heat-softened thermoplastic sheet is drawn or sucked over a mould. It can be used for a variety of products from chocolate box trays to acrylic baths.

Revise as you go!

- *Explain the difference between the moulding and shaping of plastics.*
- *What does GRP mean?*

- **Blow moulding**

  An extruded thermoplastic tube is heated and air is blown into it to force the plastic to take on the form of the mould in which it is enclosed.

- **Rotational moulding**

  Usually for thermoplastics. Powder is heated inside a closed mould which is then rotated around two or three axes. This forces the plastic to take the form of the surface of the mould. It can be used to make very large hollow articles.

- **Calendering**

  Usually for thermoplastics. Molten plastics are squeezed between hot rollers to form film or sheets.

- **Casting**

  Useful for thermosetting plastics. Molten plastic is poured into a mould.

- **Bending**

  Thermoplastics can be heated along a line using an electric strip heater and then folded to the desired angle. A bending jig is sometimes used to hold the plastic in position until it resets.

- **Fabrication**

  Plastics can be joined together using a variety of fixings and adhesives.

- **Coating**

  Powdered thermoplastic melts on the surface of a heated product giving it a thin film coating.

- **Forming**

  Layers of glass fibre (Glass Reinforced Plastic) matting and polyester resin can be formed over a mould. As the resin cures it will harden to give rigidity to this fibre/resin matrix. Thermoplastic can also be formed by heating the whole sheet in an oven until it becomes 'floppy'. The sheet is then pressed between two formers.

Case Study

Learn more about plastics processing by visiting **www.bpf.co.uk**

Find three products that have been made by each process and add them to your list.

Injection Moulding

Injection moulding is a process which allows large quantities of plastic components to be made quickly. Thermoplastic granules are heated until they soften. Then the material is forced under pressure into a mould. When cool, the mould is opened and a component, which is the exact shape of the cavity, is extracted. Injection moulding is one of the most important industrial processes in the mass production of plastic goods. The cost of machining the original moulds can be very high. Therefore it is necessary to sell large numbers of the products being manufactured to recover costs.

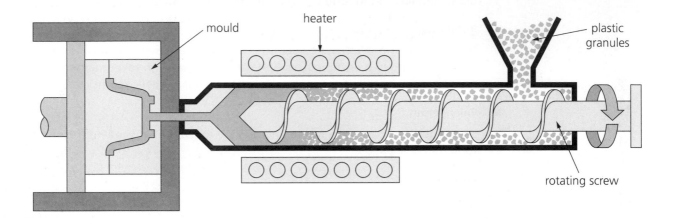

The Process

1   A feed hopper is filled with thermoplastic granules.

2   A rotating screw mechanism passes the granules through a heater.

3   The heater causes the granules to plasticise.

4   The soft plastic is injected into the mould where it is cooled (dwell time).

5   The mould is opened automatically.

6   The finished component is ejected.

7   No further finishing is required. The quality of the product is identical to the surface of the mould.

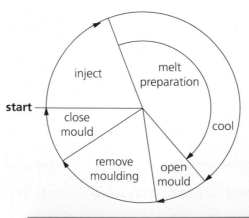

Moulding cycle

A typical injection moulding cycle is shown in the figure opposite.

The machine is inoperative (dwell time) when the melt is prepared. Also during this time the product is cooling inside the mould.

Identifying Features

Sprue marks, draw angles, mould split lines, ejection pin marks, injection mark. Webs are used for strength. A variety of surface finishes is possible from high quality shiny finish to a textured finish.

Uses

Injection moulding is a high volume, automated industrial manufacturing process used to produce more products than any other process. Components produced vary from golf tees, spoons, wash basins, buckets and product casings to small sailing dinghies.

The main casing and many other parts of this boot have been injection moulded.

Here we see a closer view of the adjustable calf support at the back of the boot. Notice the four circles made by the ejection pins. This is a clear indication that this part has been injection moulded. Also PP has been stamped on it indicating that it has been made from polypropylene.

Injection moulding is the preferred method of manufacturing the casings for domestic products. The Ross radio was designed in 1985 by Graham Thomson for Ross Electronics and was injection moulded in ABS plastic. The Durabeam torch was designed by Nick Butler in 1982 for Duracell UK and was injection moulded in black ABS plastic.

Revise as you go!

- *Why is it necessary to have tapered sides on a component that has been injection moulded?*
- *Write down three other features that you would look for to find out if a product has been injection moulded.*
- *Why is injection moulding only suitable for mass-produced products?*

Compression Moulding

Compression moulding is the process most often used for shaping thermosetting plastics such as phenol-formalehyde and urea-formaldehyde. Thermosets tend to be strong and brittle but they have a poorer impact resistance than thermoplastics. The process requires plastic to be placed into a mould cavity where it is heated and plasticised. It is then compressed into shape by a heated punch.

The Process

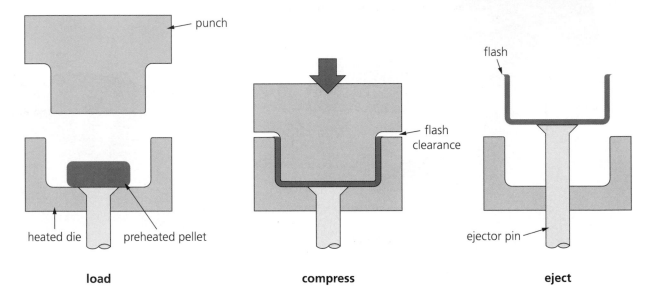

load	compress	eject

1   A measured quantity of a thermosetting plastic in powder or pellet form is placed in the highly polished cavity (female mould) and subjected to heat and pressure.

2   The material sets hard and the mould is opened.

3   The article is then removed by an automatic ejector mechanism.

Curing times vary between 0·5 and 3 minutes, reducing production times compared with injection moulding. Scrap rates are low because there are no sprues or runners. Initial tool costs are high but this is offset by low die wear. This process gives repeated precision forming with low shrinkage. Metal inserts and threads can be moulded in.

Type 300 'Cheesedish' phone designed by Jean Heiberg for Ericsson of Sweden in 1930.
The phone was compression moulded in Bakelite, which was a strong brittle plastic which would chip easily if bumped or dropped.

Materials

Restricted to thermosetting polymers: phenol-, urea- and melamine-formaldehyde; epoxy resins. Fillers, e.g. woodflour, cotton, glass, mica or talc, are added for dilution or reinforcement. Phenols are stiff and strong and can be brittle. Good electrical insulation properties.

Identifying Features

Walls of uniform thickness usually 3–6 mm. Draft of 1° minimum required. Flashes on edges. Quality finish on female mould surface.

Uses

Plastic products made using this process can resist temperature increases. Uses include automotive distributor caps, camera cases, electrical wall sockets, handles, knobs and light switches.

Electrical fittings are today compression moulded in thermosetting plastics. This gives them good insulation properties as well as a much higher melting point than thermo-plastics.

Revise as you go!
- *Briefly describe the process of compression moulding.*
- *Name two products that have been compression moulded.*

Extrusion

The extrusion process is used for products with long uniform cross sections. A variety of metals and thermo-plastics are suited to the extrusion process.

The Process

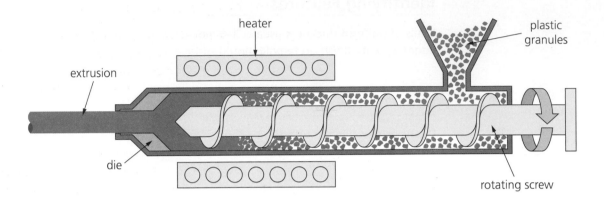

This process can be compared to squeezing toothpaste from a tube.

1   Heated compressed plastic is forced by a screw feed or hydraulic ram through a die which determines the section of the extrusion.

2   The extruded product then passes through a cooling chamber to reharden the plastic.

3   Further finishing may be required at this stage. Metals can also be extruded in a similar way.

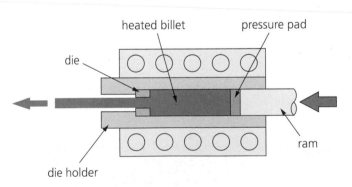

■   *Forward Extrusion*

Used for long continuous lengths. A heated billet is forced through a die. Complex shaped dies can be used.

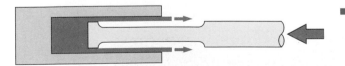

■   *Backward Extrusion*

Used for short lengths. A heated billet is extruded backwards by a smaller diameter punch.

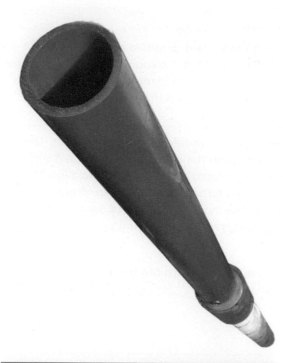

Materials

Plastic is much easier to extrude than metal because less force is required. Polythene, PVC and polypropylene are suitable thermoplastics. Suitable metals include lead, copper, brass, bronze, aluminium alloys, magnesium alloys and steel.

Identifying Features

Smooth-walled long sections with uniform thickness. Line texturisation may be evident, particularly on extruded metal products. Complex irregular profiles are produced for products such as window frames and curtain rails.

Uses

These include curtain rails, drainpipes, electric cable sheathing, fluorescent light covers, fibre for fabrics or hose pipes.

This slalom pole used in skiing was extruded in a thermoplastic. It is strong, light weight, colourful, weather resistant and not too cold to touch in more extreme conditions.

The shape of the die will determine the finished product's shape and whether it is solid or hollow.

Revise as you go!
- *Describe in your own words the process of extrusion.*
- *Name three materials that are suitable for extrusion.*

Vacuum Forming

Vacuum forming is a widely used industrial process used to mould plastics. The thin plastic sheet used in the process is produced in a variety of colours. There is no need for expensive moulds or dies to be used. Moulds are generally made from wood although steel or aluminium can be used. An additional advantage is that the process is completed in only a few minutes.

Air is removed from underneath a heated, soft and flexible thermoplastic sheet. This partial vacuum allows atmospheric pressure to push the plastic onto the mould surface. Moulds have to be well made. Sides should be tapered towards the top to allow the formed plastic to be removed easily. This taper is termed a 'draft'. Deep 'draws' require venting to avoid the problem of trapped air. The mould requires a smooth finish, radiused corners and no undercuts to allow easy removal and avoid excessive webbing and thinning.

There are various types of vacuum-forming machines which can be used depending on the size, capacity and shape of the work to be done.

The Process

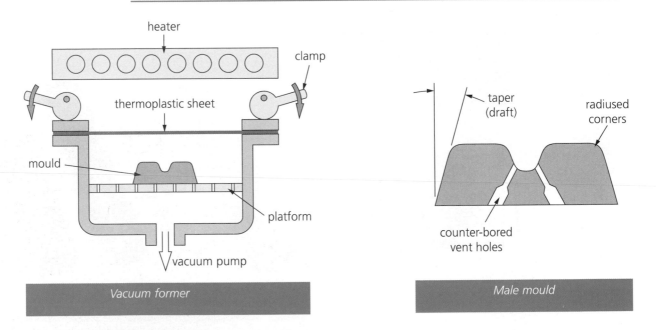

Vacuum former

Male mould

1   The plastic sheet is clamped in a frame so that there is an airtight seal over a vacuum chamber.

2   A heater is placed over the sheet and the material is heated until it becomes 'plastic'.

3   A lever is pulled, raising a platform and pushing the mould into the softened sheet.

4   A vacuum pump removes the air from the chamber allowing the sheet to form tightly around the mould.

5   The sheet is allowed to cool. Then it is unclamped and removed.

6   Excess material is trimmed off.

Vacuum forming is commonly used for packaging goods.

Materials

Most of the common thermoplastics – polythene, PVC, high density polystyrene, ABS and acrylic – are suited to the vacuum forming process.

Identifying Features

Thin sheet material is normally used. Any patterns or textures are transferred from the mould onto the product surface. Venting holes cause 'pips' on the surface. Tapers are quite pronounced and there may be evidence of thinning on the side surfaces.

Uses

Packaging items with complex deep shapes are made in this way, for example trays, dishes and margarine containers. Other examples include toys, dishes, lighting panels.

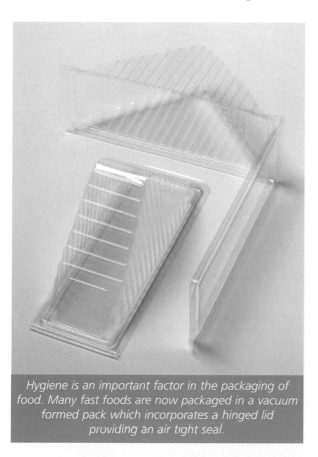

Hygiene is an important factor in the packaging of food. Many fast foods are now packaged in a vacuum formed pack which incorporates a hinged lid providing an air tight seal.

The tray shown has surface ridges, deep dividers and a lipped surround around the top edge. These features give rigidity and strength to the thin material.

Revise as you go!

- *Name five products that have been manufactured by vacuum forming.*
- *Name a plastic that is suitable for vacuum forming.*

Blow Moulding

Softened thermoplastic is forced on to the mould surfaces using compressed air. There are several variations of the process, producing articles of different sizes. The finish is never of the same standard as that of injection moulding but good mould design enables products of uniform thickness, complex shape and good quality to be produced. Blow moulding is fast and the process involves very little waste.

The Process

The process involves using a hollow length of thermoplastic material (a Parison).

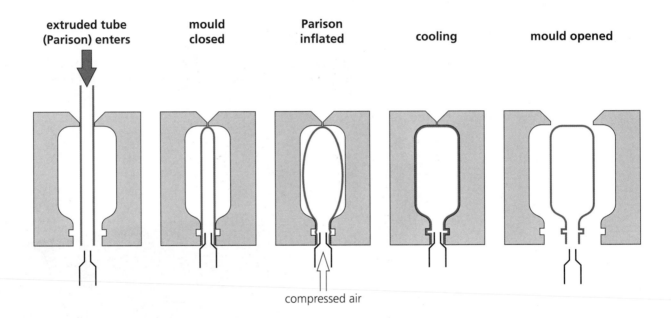

extruded tube (Parison) enters   mould closed   Parison inflated   cooling   mould opened

compressed air

1   The Parison is produced by extrusion or injection moulding and is clamped between the mould halves and inflated or blown into shape using compressed air.

2   The plastic cools on contact with the mould surface.

3   Reopening the mould ejects the shape.

The process starts again.

The plastic may cool rapidly on contact with the metal mould so the compressed air is often heated to prevent this happening prematurely. The article undergoes further processes. Flashes are removed and printing and decoration are completed. Labels coated with hot-melt adhesive can be placed in the mould before moulding.

Identifying Features

Mould separation lines. Flash lines. Almost any shape of bottle or container. Wide range of sizes. Transparent, opaque or coloured. Threaded necks are easily produced by compression moulding in the neck clamp or by injection-moulding Parisons. Long components suffer from 'draw down', making uniform wall thickness difficult to produce.

Uses

The process is widely used in mass production of bottles and liquid containers, using a variety of polymers and laminates.

Plastic bottles and liquid containers are usually made using injection blow moulding. This process can be used to produce intricate shapes on the bottles. Even the threaded necks on the bottles for the bottle tops are part of this same process.

Revise as you go!

- *Describe in your own words the process of blow moulding. Name two products that have been made by this process.*
- *Explain why blow moulding is the most suitable process for the manufacture of both products.*

Rotational Moulding

Rotational moulding is used to produce 'closed and seam free' components made from plastic polymers. There is no external pressure involved in the forming process. The products produced are hollow and stress-free and come in a wide range of shapes and sizes. The moulds are made from steel, which may be copper coated for better surface detail; aluminium for better heat transfer; electroformed nickel for best surface detail. The mould is rotated on several axes with the speed dependent on the production requirements. Large moulds have air vents to avoid the product distorting. The process is suited to small production runs and can be used for prototypes.

The Process

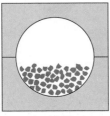 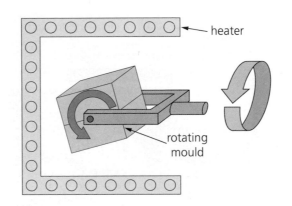 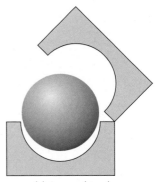

mould filled   heater / rotating mould   mould opened and product removed

1   A measured quantity of plastic powder is added to the mould.

2   The mould is closed and rotated slowly around two or three axes. This allows the plastic to be distributed over the hot mould surface.

3   The plastic melts on contact and builds up an even coating on the inside surface of the mould.

4   When the mould surface is cooled the plastic will retain its shape.

5   The mould is opened and the product is removed.

Materials

Those used include plasticised polyvinyl chloride (PVC), the most versatile and easily moulded material. It is used as a dispersion in liquid plasticiser (a 'plastisol'). Polypropylene and low density polythene and nylon are also used. Recyclability is a feature of all the materials used in this process.

Identifying Features

Rigid components may incorporate inserts for fixing. Flexible/inflatable components may incorporate valves for inflation. Detailed components will have excellent surface detail and information graphics can be incorporated in the surface finish. Effects such as wood grain, stone and leather can be produced. Mouldings should be designed to avoid sharp concave sections and thin, weak areas.

Uses

Large tanks (10,000 litres) and a range of flexible mouldings have been produced using rotational moulding techniques. Other more common products include balls and hollow plastic toys, road markers and buoys.

Rotational moulding is used to produce plastic toys and play equipment.

Revise as you go!
- *Name a suitable plastic for rotational moulding.*
- *Describe in your own words the process of rotational moulding.*
- *Name two products that have been rotational moulded.*

Mould Making

When we see a product for the first time we often think only about the functional and aesthetic qualities of the design. We may occasionally spare a thought for the effect the product will have on the environment or wonder if the product will actually sell in numbers and make money. Rarely do we consider the thought and skill that has gone into designing the mould for the product. Without an accurately designed and well made mould then the product will neither look good nor function properly and it certainly won't make any money.

Designing the Mould

The mould being designed on a 3-dimensional CAD package before manufacture begins.

A product designer will normally produce three-dimensional models and a variety of 2-D and 3-D drawings which give detailed information on their design. These are presented to the manufacturer to discuss any changes that may be required to allow the product to be made more cost effectively and more easily. Once this has been agreed the **mould designer** will transfer all the information into their own CAD system and create final drawings of the finished product.

The design of the mould starts with two blank base plates. Basically these are square section blocks of metal that are linked together by four guide pillars or tie bars, one at each corner. These base plates are standard components made from tool steel and can be ordered in a variety of sizes depending on the size of the mould being made and the pressure required to inject the plastic into it. One of the blocks will remain fixed to the moulding machine and the other will slide along the four pillars allowing the mould to be opened and closed and the product to be removed.

The movable base plate normally has the moulded component attached to it when it opens and will house the ejector pins, while the fixed base plate houses the injection holes. One of the first decisions the mould designer will have to make is to decide which side of the component will remain fixed to the movable mould. This is important, as the side closest to the movable plate will be marked by the ejector pins. This damage is usually seen as small polished circular marks on the surface. Other issues such as wall thickness, draft angles and the positions of cores to make internal spaces also need to be decided upon at this stage. A **split line** will appear on the product where the two base plates meet when in the closed position. This line can be unsightly and its position needs to be considered carefully if a secondary finishing process is to be avoided.

All of these features are included in a three-dimensional CAD drawing of the mould along with a provision for waterways. These are a series of connecting passageways running around the mould, which allow coolant to flow through them. This is essential for all moulds to keep them at the same temperature throughout the moulding process.

Revise as you go!

- *What material is used to make a mould for use in injection moulding?*
- *What do you understand by the term 'split line'?*
- *What is spark erosion used for?*

The position of the injection point and the number and position of the ejector pins are a decision for the mould designer. There are formulae and computer simulation packages that can help but the experience of the designer and his or her understanding of the restrictions set by the client are vital here.

Making the Mould

The first stage in physically making the mould involves drilling all the holes for the injection points, ejector pins, location points, waterways and seals. This is controlled directly from the drawings on the computer to a CNC machine. The base plates are then mounted on a milling cutter which again is linked to the computer drawings and the **mould cavity** is 'roughed out' usually leaving no more than an extra 0.5 of a millimetre all the way around still to be removed. This additional material is then removed on another CNC machine by a process of spark erosion. This is a very accurate process and can give a variety of surface textures.

The cost to produce a mould can start at around £20,000 for a small component. However, once made the mould becomes very durable with a life expectancy of over one million shots.

This is the fixed base plate which is attached to the moulding machine. The four guide pillars can be seen at the corners of the mould along with three angled location pins for the three sliding core plates which create the hollow cavities inside the casing. Also visible is the injection point inside the mould cavity.

Here we see the casing still attached to the movable base plate shortly after moulding. The three sliding core plates are still holding the casing. These would move away from the casing along the angled location pins as the mould opens. Notice the sprue pin where the plastic has been injected.

Shows the ejector pins in the forward position shortly after the mould has been ejected.

The finished casing. Notice the split line running around the centre of the moulding.

Metals

Metals form the major portion of the Earth's elements. They can be found combined with other elements as minerals which are mined in various ways. These metal 'ores' are processed using different methods (depending on the ore type) to produce usable materials. Gold is the only metal to be found in its pure state. All other metals are found chemically combined with other elements in the form of oxides or sulphates.

Metals are categorised as **ferrous** or **non-ferrous**. Ferrous metals contain iron as the base metal.

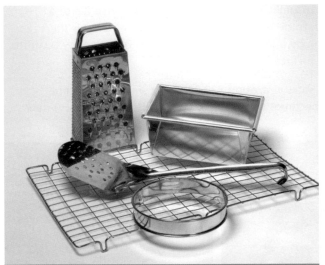

A look at some common kitchen products illustrates how metals play a vital part in our lives.

Alloys

Alloys are mixtures of metals and/or other elements combined together. Ferrous alloys range from plain carbon steels, with 98% iron, to high alloy steels, with up to 50% of other elements.

All other metals are non-ferrous and can be subdivided into light, heavy and refractory (heat resistant) alloys.

Ferrous alloys, particularly steels, form about 90% of the world's total metal usage. This is because of their low cost and versatility which is brought about by hardening and tempering.

Forms of Metal

Metals are produced in a variety of forms, e.g. rod, bar, flat strip, tube, angle and various channel sections. These forms are available in a vast range of sizes because it is difficult to change the size of any piece of metal – it takes a lot of energy to cut or soften it.

Applications

This huge variety of metals and alloys can be used in diverse applications ranging from decorative jewellery to the production of engine components. The suitability and selection of a particular metal for a product will depend on its properties.

Car parts such as engines, alloy wheels, exhausts, brake and suspension components all use different types of metals and alloys.

Revise as you go!

- *Explain the difference between hardness and toughness with regard to metals.*
- *Name five forms of supply for metal.*

Designed in 1922 by Gustaf Dalen, the Aga stove worked on the principle of heat storage with preset cooking plates for boiling. It was made primarily in cast iron and can still be bought today from selected outlets.

Properties

Properties of metals include:

elasticity	ability to return to shape after deformation
toughness	ability to withstand sudden loading (impact resistance)
brittleness	ability to be snapped easily
malleability	ability to be hammered into shape without fracturing
hardness	resistance to wear or indentation
ductility	ability to be stretched (drawn) to a reduced cross-section.

It is also important to consider the manufacturing processes available when deciding which metal will be most appropriate for a particular product.

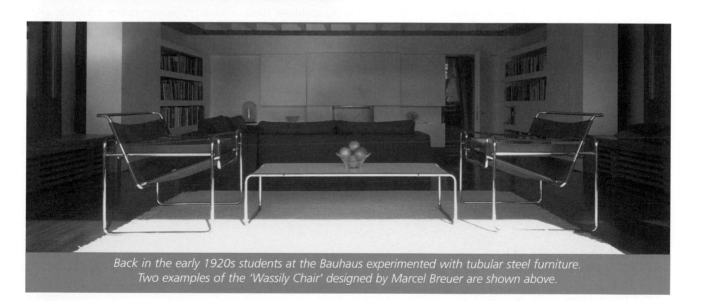

Back in the early 1920s students at the Bauhaus experimented with tubular steel furniture. Two examples of the 'Wassily Chair' designed by Marcel Breuer are shown above.

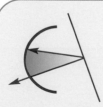

Case Study

Philippe Starck, Richard Sapper and Michael Graves have all designed products for use in the home that have been made from metals. Enter each of their names into a search engine such as **www.google.com** or **www.yahoo.com** and find three examples of products for each which you can copy into your file. Find out the names of the metals for each product you have chosen.

Ferrous Metals

Iron is the basis of all ferrous (iron-bearing) alloys. Pure iron is of little practical use as a material. Iron ore is first processed into 'pig' iron from which a range of useful materials is produced by heating and alloying processes. These include the addition and careful control of carbon content.

Only a small percentage of the pig iron that is produced is cast into shape straight from the furnace. Most cast iron is in fact derived from scrap iron and scrap steel with only some pig iron added. Most of the pig iron that is produced from the raw ore undergoes further refining processes before being turned into steel. Steel is produced by reducing the carbon content. This is done through an oxidation process where air or oxygen is passed over or through the molten metal in a furnace. The carbon combines with the oxygen to form carbon monoxide or carbon dioxide gas.

Alloying refers to the bringing together of two or more metals, often with other additive elements to improve the properties and characteristics of the new material.

Ferrous Alloys

Ferrous alloys range from plain carbon steels with 98% iron to high alloy steels with up to 50% of other elements. Alloy steels contain other elements such as chromium, nickel, molybdenum, vanadium, tungsten and manganese. These elements are added in small quantities of under 5% to improve strength or hardness. Larger quantities are added to improve corrosion resistance or wear resistance at high temperatures. Elements such as lead and manganese are used to improve the machinability of the steel. Examples of ferrous alloys are stainless steel, where chromium is the additive, and high speed steel (HSS), where tungsten is used.

It is important to know the properties of the various grades of steel so that you can select the right one to suit a particular application and method of manufacture.

Name	Composition	Properties and working characteristics	Uses
Cast iron	iron + 3.5% carbon	brittle/hard skin	machine tools, vices
Mild steel	iron + up to 0.35% carbon	malleable/ductile uniform texture	nuts, bolts, scrrews, tubes, girders, car bodies
High carbon steel	iron + up to 1.5% carbon	malleable/ductile, can be hardened and tempered	cutting tools, files, drills, saws, knives, hammers, taps and dies

Revise as you go!
- *Explain why ferrous metals rust.*
- *What finishing process could be applied to steel to prevent it from rusting?*

Charles Rennie Mackintosh used wrought ironwork extensively as both functional and decorative elements in his buildings. The piece shown here is the exterior signage for the Willow Tearoom Glasgow (1903–1904). The metal used is wrought iron (worked iron), which was named after the process by which it was made. Rods of white hot metal were hammered or rolled together producing an elongated grain structure with a high carbon content. This gave a strong malleable metal which proved resistant to the elements.

Most metal cutting tools are made from a variety of high carbon tool steels or high speed steels (HSS). These ferrous alloys give the required balance of toughness, strength and wear resistance.

This kettle with a singing whistle was designed by Richard Sapper in 1983. The main body of the kettle is stainless steel with a copper and stainless steel heat-diffusing bottom. The whistle is made from brass and the handle from polyamide.

Non-ferrous Metals

This group of metals does not contain iron and therefore will withstand moist conditions. Common examples are:

- copper, aluminium, tin and lead
- precious metals such as gold and silver
- metals used in small amounts (chromium, tantalum, mercury, platinum)
- 'new' metals (vanadium, niobium, zirconium).

Aluminium

Aluminium is the Earth's most plentiful metal. Aluminium's lightness and strength make it the most widely used non-ferrous metal. Bauxite is the only commercial source of aluminium – this ore is found in the USA, France, Australia and Africa. It is difficult to refine and requires large quantities of electrical energy (about five times that for the conversion of steel) in the smelting process.

Aluminium is alloyed with copper to form duralumin which has almost the same strength as steel but with only 30% of the weight.

Name	Composition	Properties and working characteristics	Uses
Aluminium	pure metal produced	good strength to weight ratio, casts easily	window frames, pots and pans
Copper	pure metal	ductile/malleable, low melting point, expensive	central heating pipes, electric wiring/cable, jewellery
Tin	pure metal	heavy/soft, low melting point	bearings, solder, coating sheet steel
Lead	pure metal	heavy/soft/weak, ductile/malleable, low melting point, can be cast	roof flashing, solder
Zinc	pure metal	weak, difficult to work	galvanising

Transport applications for aluminium are wide and varied. The material is lightweight and strong with no rust or corrosion problems. Aluminium is virtually maintenance free.

Other Non-Ferrous Alloys

Other common non-ferrous alloys include:

- brass (copper and zinc)
- bronze (copper and tin)
- soft solders (lead and tin).

Aluminium is one of the most economical and sustainable metals in use today. It is produced using renewable hydro-electricity and aluminium can be recycled repeatedly, saving both energy and the cost of primary production.

Aluminium is used in the storage, protection and preparation of food.

Bigger Picture

The Statue of Liberty is one of the most famous and well-known landmarks of the 20th century. The copper skin of the statue has survived almost unblemished over 100 years of exposure to the extremes of the elements.

© Royalty-Free/CORBIS

Copper is the most important electrical conductor and is also the major base metal in brass and bronze alloys. Copper possesses three important properties, namely high electrical and thermal conductivity; high ductility; and as illustrated in the case of the Statue of Liberty, high corrosion resistance.

Revise as you go!

- *Which two materials are alloyed to make duralumin?*
- *Describe how to test a metal to identify if it is ferrous or non-ferrous.*
- *Name two products that are manufactured from non-ferrous metal.*

Die Casting

Where large quantities of quality castings are required in industry, the moulds ('dies') need to be permanent. These special, alloy steel moulds are costly to produce because they are made in sections for easy removal of the components. The high operating costs involved make this process economically viable for high volume mass production where accuracy of shape, size and surface finish is essential.

Gravity Castings

Molten metal is poured into the cavity under its own weight. This produces sound, dense castings with mechanical properties superior to pressure casting (since metal enters the mould with less turbulence). This process also traps less gas than pressure casting does, leading to less porosity.

Pressure Die Casting

'Hot' chamber and 'cold' chamber processes are used. In both processes molten metal is forced into a metal die by a hydraulic ram. Thin sections and complex shapes with fine detail are possible.

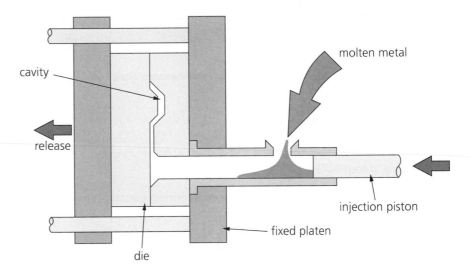

The Process

1   A measure of molten metal is poured into the charge chamber.

2   An injection piston then forces the metal into a water-cooled die through a system of sprues and runners.

3   The metal solidifies rapidly and the casting is removed, complete with its sprues and runners.

Revise as you go!
- *Write down three advantages offered to a designer by die casting.*
- *Name two features you would look for on a product to identify that it has been die cast.*

Materials

Materials used in this process include low melting temperature alloys, lead, zinc, aluminium and brass alloys.

Identifying Features

Section hair lines, ejector pin marks, flashes caused by leakages left on internal surfaces (these do not interfere with performance or appearance), and sprue and runner marks.

This is a 1:32 scale model of a Spitfire MK11A. It is marketed as 'a detailed die cast model for the adult collector'. The model shows the fine detail and high quality finish achieved by the die casting process.

The sharpener is left as cast with no secondary processes or finishes required. The pipe cutter and the nutcracker have been finished with enamel paint prior to assembly.

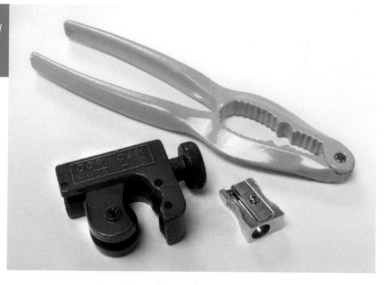

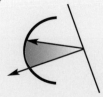

Case Study

To find out more about die casting visit **www.diecasting.org/faq**

Use this site to find out what advantages die casting has over other manufacturing methods. Write these into your file.

Sand Casting

Sand casting is the most frequently used metal casting process. 'Green' foundry sand is a blend of silica grains, clay and water. The term 'green' describes the damp quality which bonds the sand together. Oil-bound sand gives excellent results but is relatively expensive and difficult to reconstitute. There is an element of waste involved as the sand that is in contact with the hot metal will burn. This burned sand needs to be scraped out and disposed of.

The quality of the casting produced depends on the quality of the pattern. These are normally made in wood. The pattern requires radiused corners, drafted sides and a good surface finish. The sand mould is produced around the pattern, which is removed to leave a cavity. Molten metal is poured into the mould and solidifies. When cold, the mould is broken up to retrieve the casting.

The Process

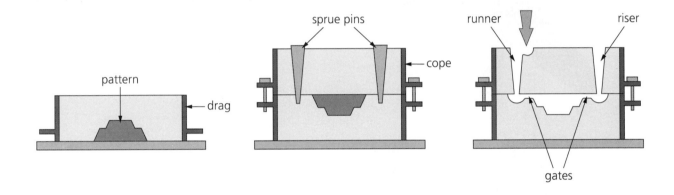

1   Place the pattern centrally in the drag.

2   Pack sand around the pattern.

3   Turn the drag over and attach the cope.

4   Insert sprue pins and pack sand around them.

5   Remove the sprue pins.

6   Split the moulding box and cut 'gates'.

7   Remove the pattern to leave a cavity.

8   Reassemble the cope so that the mould is ready to receive the molten metal.

9   Pour the molten metal into the runner. The melt fills the mould and exits, along with any gases, via the riser.

Revise as you go!
- *Why is sand casting not suitable for the mass production of products?*
- *What are the requirements of a pattern to be used for sand casting?*

Materials

Iron, aluminium and non-ferrous alloys are most widely used in sand casting. Exceptions include refractory (able to withstand high temperatures) metals such as titanium. Precious metals (e.g. gold) lend themselves to casting.

Identifying Features

Complex 3-D components. Mainly solid but internal shapes can be produced using cores. Thin sections are difficult to mould. Surface texture can be poor. Draft angles, fillets, rounded corners and strengthening webs will be evident and will echo the pattern requirements. Other recognisable features include bosses and porous surface textures. Fettle marks, due to the removal of runners and risers, may be visible.

Uses

Casting is a versatile process using the material properties in the manufacture of engine parts, tools and decorative jewellery. Multiple mould patterns decrease production time thus lowering production costs.

The photograph holder/desk tidy was designed and made by an S5 pupil. The spherical base was cast in aluminium in two separate pieces. The polished finish was produced mechanically requiring considerable time and effort. Aluminium sand casting is suited to workshop-based products because of the low melting point of the material.

Press Forming

Press forming involves squeezing sheet metal between two matched metal moulds (dies). This gives a very strong, shell-like structure. One die is the mirror image of the other, apart from an allowance for the thickness of the material being formed. The machining of these dies is a specialised skill. They can be complicated and therefore difficult and time-consuming to make. This makes them very expensive to produce. Rubber blocks can be substituted for one die in certain, more straightforward, applications. In this case, the metal to be formed (e.g. aluminium, copper, brass) must be annealed first.

The Process

The sheet metal component starts out as a flat sheet or strip.

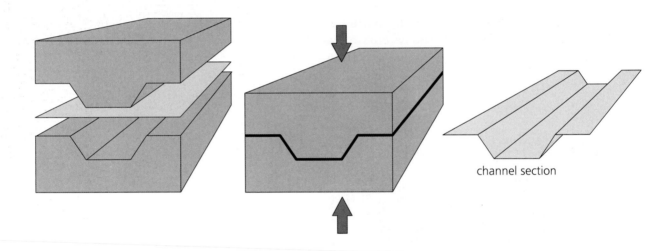

channel section

1   A blank is cut to the required size.

2   The blank is placed in a press.

3   The product is formed using immense force. One thousand tonnes are required to manipulate 3·5 mm thick steel plate.

The complete forming process may take several additional stages of operations to form, draw (stretch) and pierce the material into its final shape.

Materials

Sheet metals: various steels, aluminium alloys, brass, copper.

Identifying Features

Sudden directional changes, i.e. sharp bends and deep draws, are avoided to minimise overstretching the walls of the product. Different operations, e.g. flanges, ribs, piercing, can be identified.

Uses

Products used in many everyday activities are easily identifiable. These range from pans, kettles and stainless steel kitchen sinks to car bodies and aircraft panels.

Industrial presses generate immense force, sometimes up to 1000 tons. The tooling for the press is made from tool steel (hardened carbon steel). This may be chrome plated to improve their resistance to wear.

Complex press-formed products like this stainless steel kitchen sink require to be formed in stages. The end result is a very strong and rigid shell structure. Car bodies are made this way as are many domestic products such as pans and kettles.

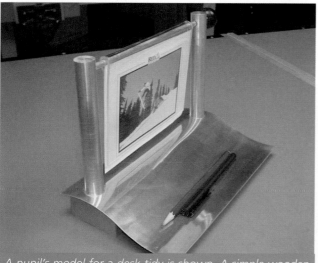

A pupil's model for a desk tidy is shown. A simple wooden mould was made from a solid block of timber to press the curved metal tray.

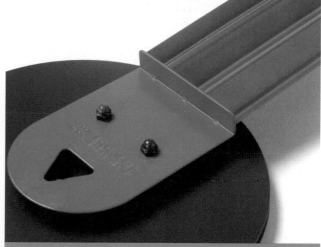

The handle of this small mirror has been press formed making it a much more rigid structure which is less likely to distort when held in the hand. It has been tack welded to the 'L' shaped back and spray painted.

Revise as you go!

- *Describe how press forming can be used to make sheet material more rigid.*
- *Name two products that have been press formed.*

Piercing and Blanking

Piercing and blanking are essentially the same process, involving the stamping of shapes out of sheet metal or metal strip. The differences in the process simply depend on which bit of metal is to be kept: in piercing a shaped hole is made in the metal, whereas in blanking a shape is stamped out of the metal and then used. In both processes, metal is placed between a hardened alloy steel **punch** and a **matching die**. A short, controlled force is provided by a hydraulically operated press, and the punch shears the metal in a cutting action around the edges of the die.

The Process

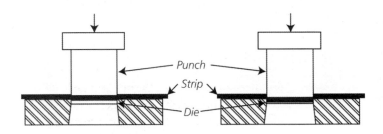

Piercing

The punch and die are shown here in the closed position. Notice how the punch just fits into the die but does not enter it, stopping instead as soon as the metal has been cut. Accurate alignment of the two is essential.

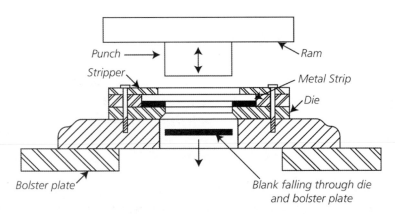

Blanking

The main components used for blanking in mass production are a punch, a die and a stripper plate. The stripper plate prevents the metal 'riding up' the die on its upward travel. The die is attached to the main press by means of a bolster plate. The punch is attached to a movable ram.

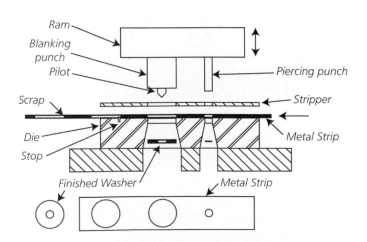

Progressive Piercing and Blanking

Many products require to be both pierced and blanked. This is often done in the same press by first piercing the metal, and then moving it along to another die and blanking out the desired shape. This process is called **progressive piercing and blanking**.

1   The metal strip is fed into the first die.

2   A hole is pierced in the metal on the first stroke of the ram.

3   The ram rises and metal is moved into position over the blanking die.

4   Accurate alignment is essential here.

5   The punch descends and the completed component (in this case a washer) is blanked from the metal strip. At the same time a hole is pierced in the next washer.

6   Piercing is normally done before blanking, as this minimises the risk of fracturing the metal.

Some examples of products produced in this way are shown below.

A washer, an Alessi key tab and a spokeshave blade.

Materials

Most types of metals can be pierced and blanked in sheet or strip form. The metal is normally annealed first so as to minimise the risk of fracture or tearing.

Identifying Features

A sheared surface will show two distinct areas of **deformation** and **fracture**. With the correct clearance angles in the punch, this can be minimised to give a reasonably smooth edge which will require no further finishing.

Uses

Uses of piercing and blanking include component parts for a variety of tool and products. Often products made from sheet metal that have been press formed are pierced to give a decorative finish.

Revise as you go!

* *What is the difference between piercing and blanking?*
  What type of material is best suited to piercing and blanking?

* *Give two reasons why the above processes are suitable for the products illustrated on these pages.*

Case Study

The Italian design firm Alessi specialise in innovative and eye-catching household products and accessories. Go to **www.alessi.com** and find three further examples of products manufactured using the piercing or blanking processes and add these to your file.

Drop Forging

Impression-die drop forging is an industrial process used in the production of high quality, strong metal components or products. The main advantages are that components can be accurately repeated using specially shaped dies to control the flow of metal; the need for highly skilled craftsmen is thus eliminated.

The Process

The dies used are very expensive to produce. High alloy steels are required to prevent heat loss which causes them to wear too quickly under impact loads.

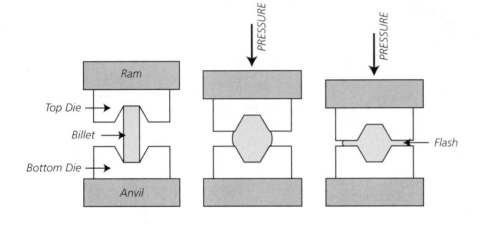

1 A hot metal billet is placed between the dies.

2 The hot metal is forced into the cavity using a power driven hammer. Note that the process may take more than one operation using a succession of dies.

3 Excess metal is squeezed out forming a **flashing** around the parting line of the two dies. The amount of flashing is determined by die wear and the quantity of excess metal.

4 When the forging is complete the flash is removed using a trimming die.

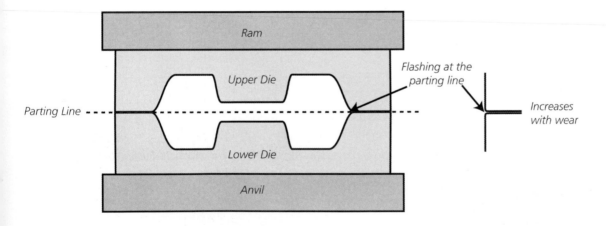

Materials

Most metals in alloy form are suited to the drop forging process. Alloy steels and copper alloys are most common.

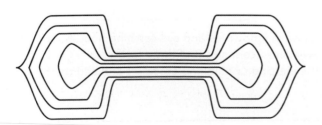

Identifying Features

The function of the product may indicate that drop forging is the most appropriate process for manufacture, i.e. the product or certain parts of the product may require compressive or tensile force to be used. Strength to weight ratio is a consideration. Visually there may well be evidence of flashing and flash removal around the edges of the product. Quality products may have undergone further finishing to eliminate visual evidence of die parting lines.

Uses

Drop forging metal increases its strength. The grain structure of the metal is changed to follow the outer contour of the component. This provides greater scope for the design of high quality metal products. Examples range from hand tools such as spanners and plumbing fittings – where the absence of porosity is particularly advantageous – to high quality cutlery and domestic appliances.

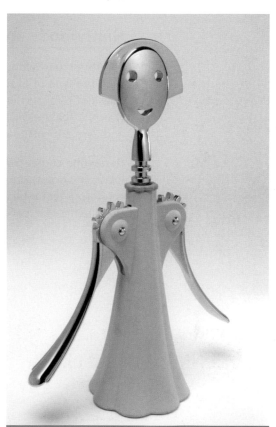

Corkscrews are known to break due to the repeated action of twisting and leverage. Here the arms and head of the 'Anna G' corkscrew have been drop forged to take advantage of the high tensile strength associated with this process. Secondary finishing has removed evidence of flashing.

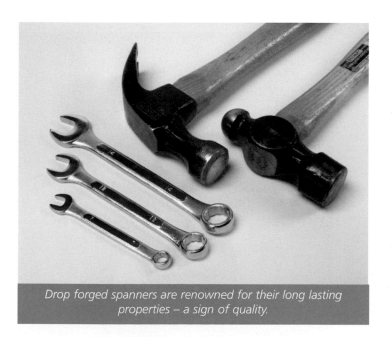

Drop forged spanners are renowned for their long lasting properties – a sign of quality.

Revise as you go!
- *What advantages does drop forging offer in the manufacture of tools?*
- *Describe how the grain structure of metal will change after being drop forged.*

Wood

Wood is an extremely useful natural material. It is hard and fibrous in nature and is made up of cells consisting of cellulose (natural resin) and lignin (the essential hard organic fibre). Wood is a natural polymer.

There are three classifications of wood to be considered. These are:

- **Hardwoods** – slow-growing (100 years) from warmer climates
- **Softwoods** – quick-growing (30 years)
- **Manufactured boards** – man-made composites.

Hardwoods and Softwoods

The terms 'hardwood' and 'softwood' refer to the rates at which the trees grow, rather than the type of prepared timber produced from them. This is a botanical division and does not refer to the wood's working properties. Balsa is an example of a hardwood, which is lightweight and easily worked and pitch pine is a softwood, which is heavy and very difficult to work.

Hardwood comes from broad-leaved trees which may be deciduous (shedding their leaves in winter) or evergreen (in leaf throughout the year). Softwood comes from coniferous (cone-bearing) trees, most of which (apart from larch) are evergreen with thin needle-like leaves.

The original Suzy Stool designed by Adrian Reed was made from beech. Beech is a close-grained hardwood making it a very strong timber with less tendency to warp. This makes it particularly suitable for the thin sections used in this stool.

Tropical hardwoods grow more quickly and to a greater size but their use has been heavily criticised by environmentalists because it contributes to the problems of deforestation. The management of wood as a sustainable, renewable resource is therefore a vital ecological issue, one which is important to us all. Forests that are not replanted are lost for all time. This is affecting the atmosphere, soil erosion, rivers, drainage and, potentially, the future well-being of the planet.

Each species of tree provides a different timber. These different timbers vary in colour, grain pattern, texture, strength, weight, stability, durability, ease of working and cost. These characteristics can be used in evaluating the appeal of the timber selected and its suitability in a particular design context.

Producing Timber

Trees are converted to usable timber by logging, sawing and seasoning. Unseasoned timber twists and splits because it is hygroscopic: that is, it takes in moisture in a moist atmosphere and gives out moisture in a dry atmosphere.

When first cut, wood has excess sap and moisture which is then dried out in controlled conditions, in natural air or in drying kilns. This gives a stable material, which is sold in rough or planed sizes as planks and boards. Other forms, such as strips, squares and a variety of mouldings, are also available.

Manufactured Boards

Manufactured boards are strong, stable and economical. They are particularly suited to the mass production of furniture as boards are available in large widths. Ecologically they can be seen as being beneficial as they use up the waste products from the sawmill, which are made into particles and fibreboard.

Revise as you go!
- *Solid timber is still used to produce high quality items of furniture. What aesthetic features of wood make it suitable for this purpose?*
- *Why is it necessary to apply a surface finish to solid timber?*

Softwoods

Softwoods are mostly produced from evergreen conifers with thin needle-like leaves. These trees are grown in regions of the Northern Hemisphere, such as Scandinavia, Canada and northern Europe, which have cold climates, and at high altitudes elsewhere.

Softwood tree growth is much quicker than that of hardwood trees and most softwood trees become mature enough for felling in under 30 years. Softwoods are relatively cheap, and are also easier to sustain by replanting.

Softwoods can be easily identified by their open grain pattern and light colour.

Straight grain gives a stronger timber which, being knot-free, is easier to cut and shape.

In pinewood, knots are produced where branches join the tree trunk. Softwood trees can be made to grow knotless and straight-grained by planting them closer together. This type of cultivation can be seen in Forestry Commission plantations. Side branches are discouraged by the lack of space and poor penetration of sunlight. Selective felling allows trees to grow in girth and height.

Purpose-built spindle moulding machines have been used to cut the decorative edges and panels seen in this range of pine furniture. Cutters are shaped to the required profile then clamped in a heavy duty cutter block which rotates at high speed giving a good finish to the profiled edge. The cutter block is mounted on a vertical spindle just above the worktable; blades are interchangeable depending on the shape required.

Common Softwoods

Name	Origin/colour	Properties and working characteristics	Uses
Scots pine	Northern Europe, Russia cream, pale brown	straight grained but knotty, fairly strong, easy to work	furniture, joinery, construction work
Red cedar	Canada, USA dark, reddish brown	light, soft, weak natural oils make it weather-durable	exterior shingles, cladding, sheds
Parana pine	South America pale yellow with red/brown streaks	Hard, straight, knot-free, strong and durable, smooth finish, tends to warp, expensive	quality interior joinery: staircases, built-in furniture, lathework
Spruce (whitewood)	Northern Europe, America creamy white	fairly strong, small hard knots, resistent to splitting, resin pockets, not durable	construction, general indoor work, whitewood furniture

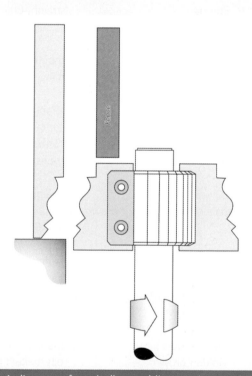

A diagram of a spindle moulding cutting machine.

Revise as you go!

- Softwoods can be grown straight-grained and knotless. Give one advantage and one disadvantage of this for the furniture maker.
- Describe how a spindle moulder can be used to enhance the appearance of wood.

Hardwoods

Hardwoods are produced from deciduous trees (trees which shed their leaves annually) and evergreen broad-leaved trees. These trees are grown in regions with warm temperate climates such as parts of Europe, New Zealand and Chile, and in tropical regions of Central and South America, Africa and Asia.

Hardwood tree growth is generally slow, taking around 100 years. This makes hardwood expensive. Tropical hardwoods retain their leaves and therefore grow more quickly and much larger in girth and height. There are ecological issues to be considered when opting to use tropical timbers, and the destruction of the world's rainforests has led to a shortage of tropical hardwoods. There is now global recognition that only sustainable sources of natural timbers (timbers grown in well-managed forests and plantations) should be used.

Hardwoods generally have more attractive grain structures, textures and colours, and greater durability than softwoods.

Name	Origin/colour	Properties and working characteristics	Uses
Beech	Europe whitish pink to pale brown	straight grained, even texture, strong	furniture, steam-bending, turnery
Elm	Europe light, reddish brown	tough, durable, cross-grained, difficult to work	turnery, furniture, outdoor uses
Oak	Europe: light brown Japan: pinky-brown	strong, durable, hard, tough, contains tannic acid which corrodes steel leaving blue stains	furniture, flooring, boat building, veneers
Ash	Europe pale cream and light brown	straight grained, coarse texture, good elasticity, works and finishes well	sports equipment, tool handles, cabinet making, laminating
Mahogany	Central & South America, W. Indies, W Africa pink reddish brown to deep brown	fairly strong, medium weight, easy to work, durable, some difficult interlocking grain, prone to warping	available in long wide boards. furniture, shop fittings, panelling, veneers
Teak	Burma, India Golden brown	hard, strong, durable, natural oils make it resistant to water, acids and alkalis, works well but blunts tools quickly	interior/exterior furniture, boat building, laboratory euipment
Walnut	Europe, USA yellow, brown, bronze, dark lines	attractive grain, cross grain can make finishing difficult	veneers, furniture, gunstocks

The bentwood Vienna Chair No. 14 made from beechwood by Michael Thonet (1859). Michael Thonet invented a method of steaming beechwood rods making them pliable. He was probably the first to introduce the notion of kit furniture.

Rietveld experimented with strict geometric structures in his furniture design. The beechwood used in this chair is precut in standard dimensions.

Revise as you go!
- Name five hardwoods.
- Give one reason why hardwoods can be so expensive.

Manufactured Boards

Manufactured boards are now extensively used in industry and in the home. These relatively new materials are categorised as laminated particle and fibreboards and are known as composites. Generally, these materials are manufactured using natural timber in thin sheets or particles, which are bonded with a resin, compressed and heated. The bonding agent has a devastating effect on normal tools and so tungsten carbide tipped tools are used in machine operations. These products are environmentally friendly in that they are often produced from waste products such as sawdust, bark and off-cuts.

Advantages

- cheap
- stable (in warm, centrally-heated environments)
- thin veneers of expensive timbers can be used as top, decorative layers
- boards are available in large sheets (1220 x 2240 and 1550 x 1550)

Veneer

Disadvantages

- edges require 'facings'
- repair and maintenance can be difficult

Revise as you go!
- *Describe two disadvantages of using manufactured boards in the manufacture of furniture.*
- *Name three manufactured boards and explain how colour could be added to the surface of each.*

The 'Casablanca' unit by Ettore Sotsass for the Memphis collection in 1981. Small boards are covered in laminated plastic which were put together like a child's game.

Common Manufactured Boards

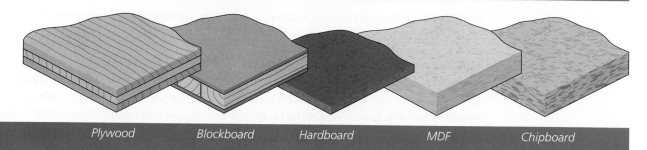

Plywood   Blockboard   Hardboard   MDF   Chipboard

Name	Composition	Properties and working characteristics	Uses
Plywood	thin veneers, cross-laminated using an odd number of layers	stable, strong and easy to machine	furniture, joinery, construction work
Blockboard	25mm strips glued together and faced with ply	stiff and heavy, good load-bearing capabilities	furniture, worktops, veneer groundwork
Hardboard	highly compressed wood fibres	cardboard-like, weak and brittle	low-cost furniture parts, e.g. cabinet backs, drawer bottoms
MDF (Medium Density Fibreboard)	compressed wood fibres	easily machined, moulded and painted	general carcass/painted work, veneer ground
Chipboard	compressed wood chips	stiffness and strength vary with density	furniture carcassing, good veneer ground

Manufactured boards are used extensively in the design of flat pack furniture. Most of the IKEA range is designed flat pack – this saves space in storage and transit costs are lower. Customers can take their purchases home and assemble the furniture themselves. All they usually need is an allen key and sometimes a screwdriver.

Case Study

Plywood has been around since the 1850s and has been extensively used in furniture design since then. Visit the Design Museum website at **www.designmuseum.org/** on their Design at the Design Museum page and find three examples of furniture made from plywood. Add these to your file.

Adhesives

Adhesives are used to bind two materials together, usually permanently. The selection of an adhesive depends on the purpose of the product and the material to be joined. Wood glues join timber products (wood to wood); other adhesives, such as epoxy resins, will bond dissimilar materials. Some will allow time for repositioning and adjustment while others bond instantly on contact. The cramping method and the curing time are as important as the correct choice of adhesive. Adhesives will not normally bond to greasy or wet surfaces and this can be one reason for failed bonding.

Types of Adhesive

- **PVA** (polyvinyl acetate) **glue**

   This is the most widely used wood glue. It is sold ready-mixed, white, and water-soluble. It is strong and does not stain. Excess is wiped off with a damp cloth. It requires light cramping and sets in approximately 2 hours, depending on temperature. PVA glue can also be used to seal the edges of MDF before painting. A waterproof version of this glue is now available.

- **Tensol cements**

   These are **solvent-based** adhesives for joining thermoplastics. There is a range of these special cements available and the use of the correct adhesive is important (e.g. Tensol 12 for acrylic). The area of gluing surface will affect the strength: use overlaps and position joints away from corners.

- **Epoxy resin**

   This is a two-part adhesive for unlike materials. It will bond glass, ceramics, wood, metal, and hard thermosetting plastics. Mixing the resin and hardener triggers a chemical reaction which sets the adhesive. Epoxies are waterproof with good gap filling and electrical insulation properties. The use of an epoxy resin glue is normally restricted to small-scale applications because of the high cost. They are not suited to thermoplastics.

- **Contact** (impact) **adhesive**

   These adhesives, such as Evostick, are used to fix plastic laminates (melamine) and other sheet and strip materials. Surfaces are coated and left until 'touch' dry. Bonding is immediate and correct positioning is therefore essential. Most contact adhesives give off noxious fumes so they should only be used in well ventilated areas.

- **Hot melt glue**

   This is supplied in glue-stick form and is applied using a hot glue gun. It is popular for modelling and temporary work. It has tended to be messy, weak and gives a poor finish. However, hot melt glue guns are increasingly used in many furniture factories as permanent adhesive joining methods.

Revise as you go!
- *Describe how epoxy resin would be prepared before being used to join two parts together.*
- *Write down three things that should be considered before deciding which glue to choose.*

■ **Double-sided tape**

This is being used increasingly for joining large flat areas of metal and plastics. Clean surfaces are essential for effective joining.

Using Adhesive

■ Ensure the surfaces are clean, dry and free from grease.

■ Do not apply finishes to the surfaces to be joined.

■ Roughen the surfaces to provide a 'key'.

■ Select and use the correct adhesive. Read the manufacturer's instructions.

■ Assemble dry and prepare a sequential procedure before applying adhesive.

■ Check for squareness and alignment.

The choice of an adhesive will depend on:

■ availability and cost

■ the strength of the join required

■ the environment where it is to be used

■ the materials that are to be joined.

The material/adhesive matrix below can help with choosing a suitable adhesive but it should be noted that there are many new adhesives on the market that will suit a variety of purposes.

	PVA	Tensol	Epoxy	Contact	Hot melt	Double sided tape
Metal to:						
Fabrics			✓✓	✓✓		✓
Metals			✓✓✓	✓✓		✓✓
Thermoplastics			✓✓✓			✓✓
Thermosets			✓✓✓	✓		✓✓
Wood	✓		✓✓✓	✓✓	✓✓	✓
Manufactured boards			✓✓	✓✓✓	✓✓	✓
Wood to:						
Fabrics	✓		✓✓✓	✓✓		✓✓
Metals	✓		✓✓✓	✓✓		✓✓
Thermoplastics				✓✓	✓✓	✓✓
Thermosets			✓✓✓	✓✓✓	✓✓	✓✓
Wood	✓✓✓		✓✓✓	✓		✓✓
Manufactured boards	✓✓✓		✓✓✓	✓		✓✓
Plastics to:						
Fabrics			✓✓	✓✓		✓✓
Metals			✓✓	✓✓		✓✓
Thermoplastics		✓✓✓	✓✓			✓✓
Thermosets		✓✓✓	✓✓			✓✓
Wood			✓✓✓			✓✓
Manufactured boards			✓✓			✓✓

Joining Materials

The manufacture of most products requires joining together of materials. Part of the designer's role is to select the most appropriate method.

- **Permanent** joining methods include adhesives, arc welding, fitted joints, riveting, spot welding.
- **Non-permanent** methods include nuts, bolts and screws.

Design Considerations

- Is the bond or joint to be permanent, semipermanent or temporary?
- Is there to be allowance for movement?
- Are the materials similar or dissimilar?
- Will ambient conditions, e.g. weather, affect the joint?

Adhesives

Common adhesive	Use
Polyvinyl acetate	General purpose wood glue. Thin for use with paper or card. Sets in 1 hour +.
Glue gun	Glue stick electrically heated. Quick-setting for small surfaces.
Tensol cement	Solvent for acrylic. Hardens quickly.
Epoxy resin	Epoxy resins are synthetic polymers. Resin and hardener are mixed in equal quantities. Sticks to almost anything. Expensive.
Synthetic resins	'One shot' (mix with water) amd 'Two shot' (resin + hardener, spread on separate surfaces). For strong laminated joints.
Contact adhesive	Also called 'impact' adhesive. when bought together, the surfaces cannot be moved for adjustment. assembly must be precise. Bonds plastic laminates to particle boards.
Super glue	Bonds on contact. Used on small surfaces.
Balsa cement	Quick-setting cement for balsa modelling.
Polystyrene adhesive	Suited to solid polystyrene (as in model kits), not expanded polystyrene.
Polyvinyl chloride	Mainly for joining PVC pipes

Fixings

Mechanical knock down fixings are generally used on square cut butt joints on manufactured boards. No glue is required but accurately drilled holes are essential. Knock-down fixings (fittings) make assembly straight forward and have the added advantage that dismantling a product is possible

Welding

Soldering, brazing and welding techniques are used mainly to join metals. Some thermoplastics can also be joined in this way.

■ Arc Welding

Heat is obtained by an electric arc via a transformer. One lead is attached to the work and the other to a grip holding a welding rod. An arc is formed when the end of the rod is brought near the work. The heat melts the parent metal and the filler rod together. The rod is coated with flux to prevent oxidation.

■ Spot Welding

The metal is heated and fused together between two copper electrodes. Used on thin gauge mild steel, e.g. car bodies.

Riveting

There are two methods. The traditional method uses soft iron, aluminium or copper for snap, countersunk and flat head rivets in conjunction with a hammer and rivet 'set'. Where the use of a hammer is to be avoided, controlled pressure is applied to a 'pop rivet' using a pop-riveting 'gun'. Also used for 'blind' riveting.

Fitted Joints

Wood joints are classified as being used for frame or carcass construction.

- **Frame joints**: mortise and tenon, tee halving, dovetail halving, bridle.
- **Carcass joints**: dovetail, housing, dowelling.

Most joints require an adhesive to make them permanent.

Bolts

The screw thread has the advantage of enabling items to be taken apart for inspection or maintenance purposes. Nuts, bolts and set screws can be obtained in various forms. There are numerous designs of spanners for use with square- and hexagonal-headed nuts and bolts, just as there are keys for socket screws.

Screws

Screws are used to fasten together boards, panels and fittings such as hinges and brackets. Pieces can be taken apart and reassembled without damage. Screwdrivers are available in a variety of blade types, e.g. slot and pozidrive. Effort in driving screws home can be minimised by using electrically powered 'screw guns'.

Other Things to Consider

- permanent, semi-permanent or temporary?
- type(s) of material(s)
- allow for movement
- surface area
- indoor or outdoor?
- are cramps to be used?
- time (setting time).

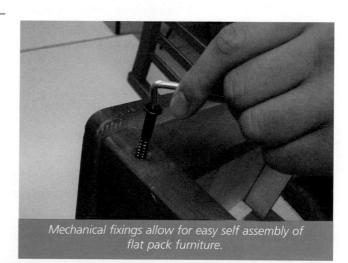

Mechanical fixings allow for easy self assembly of flat pack furniture.

Revise as you go!

- *Explain why traditional methods of joining woods and metals are being used less, particularly by bigger companies.*
- *Give an example of a product that has been joined together by knock-down fittings.*

Recycling Materials

Product designers have to be aware of the effect their work will have on the environment. They have an important role to play in helping to find solutions to the global problems faced by our planet today. These problems are often referred to as 'green issues' and can be summarised as:

- energy consumption
- pollution
- conservation of natural resources
- waste disposal.

One way they can contribute to solving these problems is by designing products that can be **recycled**.

The world's natural resources are being depleted at a rate that cannot be sustained. Oil, coal, gas, timber and ores, which are the primary source of the materials used in manufacture, are a dwindling natural resource. This problem is shared by all designers and they must aim to preserve these resources in addition to minimising the pollution caused by processing them into the materials used to manufacture today's products.

This product is made from a biodegradable material. A bacterial action causes the material to break down into carbon dioxide and water.

All products have a limited **life span**. It makes good sense to extend this wherever possible through good storage, maintenance and repairs. How the product is to be disposed of at the end of its useful life should also be part an overall design strategy so as to reduce waste and further pollution.

Waste Management

Waste management is a growing concern for councils and local authorities. The collection, transportation and sorting of recyclable waste can be so expensive that the process is not viable. Increasingly educated consumers are objecting to disposal by **landfill** and **dumping**, where there are no benefits, and to a lesser degree **incineration**, where toxic gases can be released and residual dangerous metal pollutants can be left requiring safe disposal in special sites.

What can be done?

- The most effective way of dealing with the problem is not to create the waste in the first place.
- Reusing and repairing old products will undoubtedly prolong the products' life.
- Metals and plastics (as well as paper, card and fabrics) can be **recycled** to produce new materials.

Revise as you go!

- *Write down three areas that should be considered in relation to 'green issues' in product design.*
- *With regard to the recycling of materials describe what is meant by (a) reduce (b) reuse and (c) reconstitute.*
- *Give four examples of how a designer could design a product to make it more suitable for recycling.*

Recycling Targets: the Three REs of REcycling

The recycling targets are to **REduce** , **REuse** and **REconstitute**

- **Reduce** the amount of materials used in product design by making them thinner, lighter and smaller.

- **Reduce** the amount of energy used in the manufacturing process.

- **Reduce** the amount of packaging used.

- **Reuse** parts and components reclaimed from the product once it has reached the end of its useful life.

- **Reconstitute** materials recovered from products which are no longer useful. This will minimise the need for primary material production.

Designing for Recycling

General guidelines

- Design products which have products and parts that are easy to assemble and dismantle.

- Reduce the amount of different materials used in one product.

- Composite materials are difficult to recover and should be avoided where recycling is desirable.

- The accurate labelling of all materials used is important.

- Standard components such as electrical and electronic parts should be easily removed.

Designed by Trevor Baylis, this clockwork radio can generate enough power to operate without batteries or electricity.

Both the ring pull and the can are made from the same material and remain firmly attached after opening. This prevents waste and allows both parts to be recycled together.

Case Study

Everyone can play a part in reducing, reusing and recycling the amount of materials used. Visit **www.wascot.org.uk** and find six things that you can do for each of the three REs. Write these down in your file.

The Cost of Production

Any business involved in the design and manufacture of products requires information about its potential market. To make decisions it also needs accurate and reliable information regarding **costs**. To meet a rising demand by expanding production a firm must know how much that extra production will cost; without this information it will have no way of knowing whether expanding production will make a **profit** or not.

Any rise in production costs will have a direct effect on profit margins. Expenses such as wages, raw materials, insurance, factory rental, etc. must be considered and taken into account. All resources used up during the production process must be accounted for.

Costs will change over a period of time depending on whether a small amount of products are required (**short run**) or a much greater number is required (**long run**).

In the short run it is more likely that most factors will remain constant. In the long run all factors can vary. Even the capacity can be increased by extending the existing factory or buying another one, providing more space and machines for a growing work force.

Fixed Costs

Fixed costs stay the same in the short run at all levels of output; these will include machinery, and factory rent, heating and insurance. These costs remain the same whether the production is at a maximum or a minimum level (a zero level), for example when the factory is closed for a holiday period and nothing is being produced. Fixed costs do not change even if the output changes unless there are external influences such as an increase in the rate of inflation.

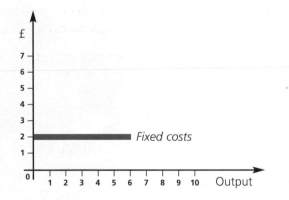

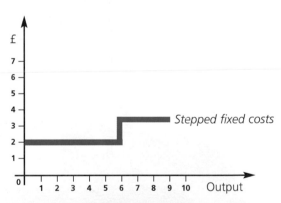

The step represents an investment in new machines or equipment for example.

The graphs illustrate how fixed costs can change over time. Fixed costs can rise if production is increased and the company decide to invest in machinery or additional equipment to cope. These new purchases will raise fixed costs as well as raising the capacity to increase production. Fixed costs can change in the long run.

Variable Costs

Variable costs refer to production costs which increase with output. The consumption of raw materials is an obvious variable cost; others include fuel, packaging and additional wages. If production stops then these variable costs will also disappear.

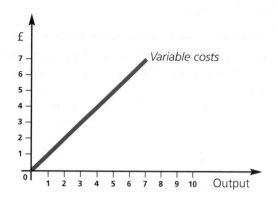

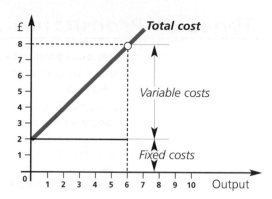

The total cost of production is found by adding together the fixed and variable costs.

An increase in output will result in a rise in cost. As output increases the fixed costs become a smaller proportion of the total costs.

Prime Costs

Prime costs or direct costs can be identified with a particular product or manufacturing process. Plastic processing usually depends on making a metal mould. Mould design is a very specialised task and it is important for the designer to consult with the production team on how best to produce the mould. It may be that changes have to be made to the product to allow it to be moulded more easily and efficiently.

The cost of making a mould can be a substantial investment, in the region of £20 000 or more for just a small part of a hand-held product. This is before the actual costs of the raw material, production, assembly, distribution and sales are taken into account. Plastic processing is therefore usually regarded as a mass production process.

Once a mould has been made it can be reused indefinitely with little or no maintenance, making the unit cost of each component very small.

The Importance of Market Research

Due to the high setup costs and other overheads involved, it is vital that proper market research is carried out to determine whether the product will sell at a competitive price in sufficient numbers to ensure a profit.

In the long run all production factors or variables are subject to the laws of economics.

The consideration of production costs is necessary for all commercial products.

Revise as you go!

- *Explain how the cost of production is affected by (a) choice of materials (b) the method of manufacturing.*
- *Give two examples of fixed costs.*
  What could cause these fixed costs to increase?

Types of Production

Different products are produced in different ways. A plastic bottle will be produced using an automated blow moulding machine whereas more complex products such as an electric fire will require several parts to be mass produced before being assembled by hand. The type of production used to manufacture a product will depend on the nature of the product, the materials it is made from, the resources available and the number to be produced.

New Methods of Production

Changes in technology have resulted in new methods of production being used. The development of the computer and of robotic welders has radically altered the way in which the motor car is made.

Car production plants have undergone complete reorganisation with the introduction of new technology. This has resulted in improved efficiency, increased production, more flexibility and an improvement in the quality of the finished product.

Production Systems

Different production systems can be described using the following terms:

- **Job Production**

  This usually refers to 'one-off' production methods where a single item or a small number of items is to be made. This method is used to produce individual items to a customer's specification, but at a high unit cost. This production process is labour intensive and highly skilled in nature.

- **Batch Production**

  Larger quantities of identical products are produced using this method. Each operation is completed for the whole batch of items before the next operation is carried out. An example of batch production might be a small furniture manufacturer who has been asked to produce 100 identical chairs. It is likely that they will divide production into several different operations. Each operation is carried out sequentially for all the chairs. Batch production can use mass-production manufacturing methods and the quantity produced can be increased or decreased easily according to demand.

- **Line Production**

  Line production means that a product is made and assembled by continuously moving it along a line. Each process is carried out and each part is added in sequence.

- **Cell Production**

  The product is manufactured and assembled by a team of people in a contained area or 'cell'. Anyone in the team can do any of the assembly or manufacturing functions required in that cell. They are also responsible as a team for quality control and the maintenance of the equipment. This method of production fits in with the 'concurrent engineering' approach.

Revise as you go!

- *Describe the difference between batch production and mass production.*
- *Why is cell production proving so popular with companies and employees?*

- **Flow Production**

This is very similar to line production except that very high volumes of products are produced. Production is often continuous, running for 24 hours each day, and fully automated. As a result, unit costs for the product are low.

Type of production characteristics			
Characteristic	**Job**	**Batch**	**Flow**
Demand	Small – one off or small numbers. Single customer or specialist market.	Demand increases. Manufacture in stages. One operation in a batch completed before moving to the next.	Regular and long term. Large volume of simplified and standardised product. Wider international market.
Quantity	One only or small market.	Batch of small quantity produced before next batch.	Larger quantities.
Variety	Very flexible. Large variety. Geared to customer specifications.	Still quite flexible. Standardised components which can vary with each new batch. Can still respond to the needs of the customer.	Inflexible. Product range limited. A variety of production lines in large scale operations can produce a wider range of products.
Workforce	Motivated. Adaptable. Work satisfaction.	Less skilled. Skilled quality control and maintenance required.	Unskilled. Repetitive task operations. Management and control systems must be efficient.
Machinery used	Less complex. Requiring operator expertise. Wide range of m/c's required for different jobs.	Less machinery but more complex. Emphasis on machine capability not skill. Retooling needed for each batch.	Technically complex. Heavy investment assumes steady demand.
Plant layout	Fixed.	By process.	By product.
Cost of production	Low fixed costs. High variable costs (labour).	Lower than job production. Efficient planning needed to ensure runs are as long as possible to spread costs.	Fixed costs are high at start up of production line. Variable costs much lower than in other methods.
Problems	Expense. Technically complex jobs can be difficult to organise.	One long batch operation will cause delay for others.	Traditional production lines are organised such that one operation depends on the next. If one section is stopped then the whole line has to stop.

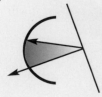

Case Study

Founded by David Colwell in 1978, Trannon specialise in batch producing steam bent furniture. Visit their website at **www.davidcolwell.com**

Find four examples of batch-produced furniture and copy them into your file.
Write down the materials used to make these items.

Manufacturing Systems

Manufacturing systems have changed dramatically over the last century; now there are a variety of systems, each with different installation and running costs. Choosing a system depends on market demands for a product, which in turn determines its volume of production. Tooling costs, factory layout and personnel also affect the choice of manufacturing system and production costs.

Small Batches

One-off or small **batches** of products are normally produced by highly skilled craftsmen in a traditional workshop environment. This is time consuming, very expensive and labour intensive. However, it offers total flexibility and the opportunity to custom make products.

Assembly Lines

Assembly lines became commonplace during the 1930s. Major manufacturing companies often employed hundreds of workers per assembly line. They organised them individually or in small groups, staying in the same place doing the same repetitive task all day. These assembly lines were very inflexible. Workers were trained to do one job and had no real concept of how the overall production was done. If there was a breakdown or hold up at one part of the line everyone had to stop. Efficiency relied on the smooth running of the whole assembly line. The first successfully produced product using this **mass-production** technique was the 'Model T Ford'.

Mechanisation

The **mechanisation** of production lines soon followed and hand-operated machines began to make production processes quicker and more accurate. Assembly lines still exist today but are either fully-or semi-**automated**. This automation depends on computer-controlled robots and machines being programmed and controlled by skilled operators. Efficiency is much greater, as is the accuracy and overall quality of the products produced.

Bigger Picture

The Osram energy-saving lamp is an example of a mass-produced product, which lends itself to automated continuous production. Energy-saving bulbs not only save on energy costs but can give up to 6 years of lamp life. They are popular with consumers who have concerns for the environment.

Flexible Manufacturing

These developments have led to more **flexible manufacturing** systems of production being used by many companies. These systems bring together computer-controlled machine tools and stock control as well as the robotic handling and assembly of parts. Machines or **manufacturing cells** are linked together, normally in a 'U' shaped formation. Production lines can be changed quickly, making it easier to produce different products or components. Other advantages include:

- teamwork and productivity are improved due to the close proximity of the personnel
- operator fatigue is reduced, eliminating human error
- productivity is improved and production flow is easily maintained
- quality assurance and control is readily checked and monitored.

The product is assembled by a team of people in a contained area or 'cell'. Anyone in the team can do any of the assembly or manufacturing functions required in that cell. They are also responsible as a team for quality control and the maintenance of the equipment. This method of production fits in with the concurrent engineering approach.

Total Quality Management

These major changes in manufacturing systems are now being driven by the concept of total quality management (TQM). This involves the elimination of the costs of inspection; of rectifying mistakes; and of preventing mistakes. All personnel are involved and the overall aim is 'to get it right first time'.

The 'Attendant's Chair' by Charles Rennie Mackintosh was designed for the attendant who took the orders from the waitresses in the Willow Tearooms in Glasgow. The lattice back was designed as a divider between the light and dark areas of the restaurant. The chair was a one off and purpose built for these reasons. pThe illustration shown is a modern replica.

Revise as you go!

- *Explain the difference between mechanisation and automation.*
- *Describe how present day flexible manufacturing systems are an improvement on the assembly line system used in the 1930s.*

Just In Time Production

Basically, Just In Time (JIT) production was first pioneered by the Japanese to reduce stock levels within factories and hence reduce costs. It is a method of manufacturing products more quickly and in the exact quantities needed to meet customer demand. Production materials arrive ready for use exactly when they are needed. This means that manufacturing firms have less capital tied up in raw materials, carry less stock and therefore require less storage space. There are no stockpiles of finished goods waiting to be dispatched. Companies who practise JIT only need to start production after they receive orders.

JIT requires good relationships between manufacturers and suppliers. Suppliers have to be flexible and able to respond immediately to manufacturers' demands. Any delay will be costly and may halt the production process. This in turn means that manufacturers must plan carefully, have accurate estimates for each stage of production and have efficient stock control systems. Information about every part and every process is essential for efficient production.

Kanban

To help JIT production to run smoothly a '**Kanban**' system is normally used. A Kanban is a method of controlling material flow. If a Kanban is set at 100, then a maximum of 100 component parts can be placed in an area at any one time. If all 100 parts are used then clearly there will be no stock available to continue with production. Therefore a minimum level must also be set for a Kanban to signal that stock has to be replenished. This visual signalling of stock levels is an important feature of this system. It reduces the need for paperwork and encourages everyone to 'keep an eye' on stock levels. Fixed quantity bins or containers can be used. If a full bin is measured at 100 parts and a quarter full bin is measured at 25 parts then every time the bin approaches the quarter level it will be replenished. This method should ensure that parts are always available.

A Kanban system is illustrated below. It shows a very simple process, which involves two assemblies. The first is assembling a nut and bolt and the second requires it to be put in a box.

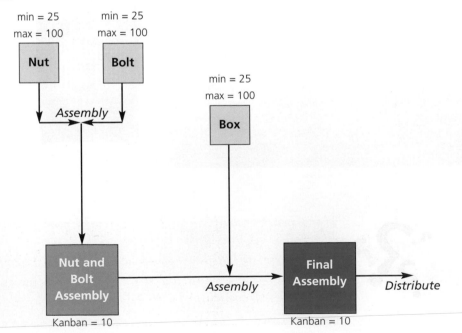

When the minimum level is reached for any of the three parts involved it is topped up. If there is a problem obtaining the parts this should be solved before the parts run out and production has to stop.

Quality control has been built into this with a Kanban of 10 being set at each of the assembly stages. This means that if a batch is found to be defective in any way then there will only be a maximum of 10 to repair or recycle before the fault is reported.

When will JIT not work?

- when the delivery of parts is not reliable
- when the distance between the supplier and factory is too great
- when the quality of the parts is not guaranteed
- when production is unstable
- when stock control is inefficient and poorly planned.

The goal of any JIT production system is to achieve:

- zero stock
- zero lead time (the time taken between an order being placed and the product delivery)
- zero defects
- zero breakdowns
- zero paperwork.

These 'five zeros' are almost impossible to achieve but they are targets to aim at. In practice, companies carry a small amount of stock (enough for a few days' production). They will, however, rely on fast, frequent and flexible delivery systems which can respond to their changing order books. The term 'lean manufacturing' is now used to describe this approach to the production of products.

Revise as you go!
- *What is meant by JIT?*
- *Under what conditions will JIT not work efficiently?*
- *In your own words describe how a Kanban works.*

Sequential and Concurrent Engineering

Sequential Engineering

When a company undertakes to design a new product, there are many stages it has to go through before the product reaches the marketplace. Many companies organise this in an orderly sequence, with each stage having to be completed before the new product is passed onto the next stage. This is referred to as **sequential engineering** or consecutive engineering.

Some of the stages in product development are shown in the diagram below.

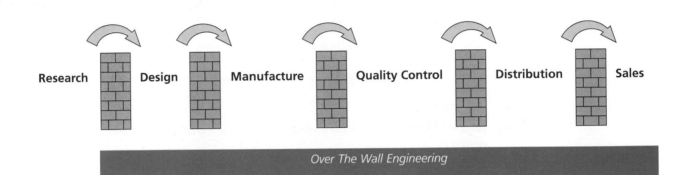

Research   Design   Manufacture   Quality Control   Distribution   Sales

Over The Wall Engineering

Some companies still work on a departmental basis, each one working very much in isolation and preparing information only relevant to the next stage in the process. No department ever has an overview of the whole process. This can be compared to passing the information over a brick wall to the next department and not being able to see it again. As a result, there is little communication between departments and often a lack of interest and concern among employees on issues such as quality control and product management.

This orderly step-by-step process will bring control to complex projects but it is very slow. In today's highly competitive marketplace this can lead to product failures and lost sales.

The barriers to information transfer need to be broken down in the interests of efficiency, quality control and to try and reduce lead times. Reorganising departments in such a way as to encourage teamwork and communication between workers can radically improve the transfer of information between workers. Integrated Information Technology systems and updated computer design packages mean that all departments have access to the contributions made by everyone in the organisation.

Revise as you go!
- *What features of sequential engineering could cause it to hold up production?*
- *Why is it important for a company to plan the manufacture of a product before starting?*
- *What advantages does concurrent engineering have over sequential engineering?*

Concurrent Engineering

The problems associated with sequential engineering can largely be overcome by companies using a concurrent engineering approach. This is a method of developing and manufacturing products using a team-based approach. Members from every department are brought together at the beginning of a project to form the product design team. Each member is a specialist in their own area but will more than likely have a knowledge of the other departments as well. They are able to interact and contribute to the project from an early stage and can begin to plan, organise and develop their own specialist inputs without having to wait for another department to finish.

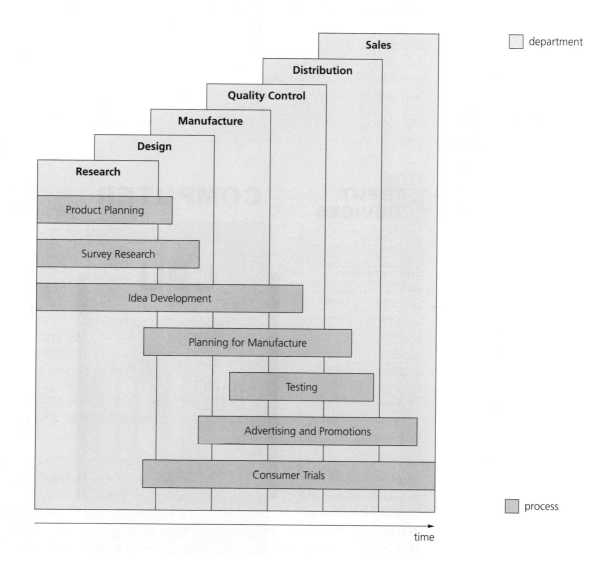

Concurrent engineering or simultaneous engineering requires departments to work closely together, overlapping the steps in the product development and manufacturing process, thus saving time and increasing effectiveness.

CAD (Computer-Aided Design)

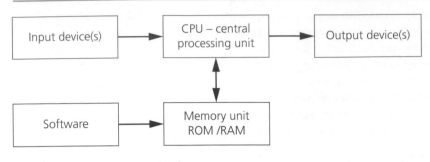

A CAD system may be regarded as a tool which allows designers to input design criteria such as sizes of components and tolerances. Standard components can be inserted from software libraries into designs. The behaviour of designs can be simulated and modifications can be made relatively easily by manipulating the stored images.

Professionals such as designers, engineers and architects, whose work involves draughting skills, have improved their productivity using computer-aided design. A typical computer system can be represented by a block diagram. However this is an oversimplification as a modern CAD system uses a variety of peripheral devices to input and output data as shown.

The type of input and output devices used will vary depending on the particular job. Many of these devices are listed in the diagram below.

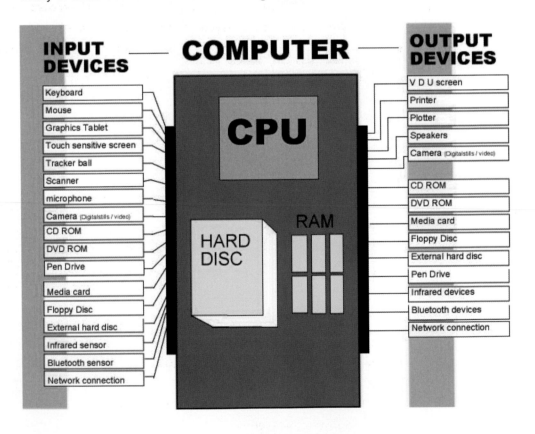

CADD (computer-aided design and drafting)

Objects can be represented as 2-D (two-dimensional) and 3-D (three-dimensional) solid or wire-frame images on screen. These can be moved and copied, and their shapes and forms manipulated and changed. Colour and animation help clarity and also with the visualisation of movement in space. A simple example of a model produced and manipulated using computer operations is shown below.

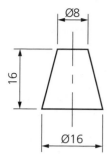

Advantages

- Design development is quicker than using traditional drawing board techniques. This releases time for the design team to produce a wider variety of proposals.

- CADD allows rapid retrieval of information using CAD libraries, databases and spreadsheets.

- Quality and accuracy of drawings are increased – output devices produce superior text and line work.

- Design quality is increased – improvements are made as a result of visual simulation of operating conditions.

- Changes can be made quickly. Prototype modelling costs are avoided.

- Drawings can be retrieved, modified and stored electronically.

- CADD allows integration with CAM, marketing, sales and production planning.

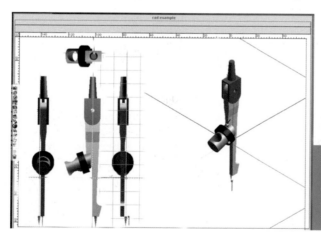

These images were drawn using 3-D modelling software. The 3-D model can be translated into a 2-D drawing with ease and this can speed up the design process.

Disadvantages

- The initial setup costs are high
- Software requires updating regularly
- Staff require training
- There is an increased risk of virus damage
- Software is expensive
- Corporate security regarding copyright and intellectual ownership can be difficult to police once the data is part of the system

Revise as you go!

- *Describe five advantages offered by a Computer-Aided Drawing and Design system.*
- *List four output devices used by a CADD operator.*

CAM (Computer-Aided Manufacture)

Computer-aided manufacture is a term used to describe production processes where machine tools and equipment are controlled by computer.

The danger and dirt associated with factory workshop floors are now largely consigned to the history books. The earliest numerically controlled (NC) machine tools of the early 1950s used punched cards and punched tapes to store the machines' instructions. Computer numerical control (CNC) was developed in the 1960s. It had the disadvantage that only large corporations could afford the necessary capital investment. This situation has changed with the computer revolution and the advent of the microprocessor. Now it is possible for each machine tool to be provided with the necessary computing power at relatively low cost. Programs can be installed in a variety of ways. Electronic storage means that new instructions can be downloaded and programmed into machines very quickly. Design modifications to suit market changes and individual customer requirements are easily introduced.

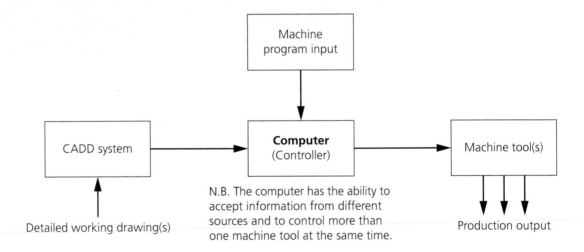

Disadvantages

- Installation and start-up costs are high, requiring capital investment.
- Skilled maintenance technicians and machine operators are required, resulting in high training costs.

Advantages

- System reliability results in higher productivity, closer tolerances and lower costs. Inspection costs are reduced with improved quality control.

- Losses due to human error are eliminated.

- Optimum speeds and feeds prolong tool life.

- Programs can easily be modified to give flexibility in production.

- There is no need for specialist positioning jigs because of the accuracy of the machines. Complex operations can be carried out easily.

- Greater output predictability results in accurate costing.

- Once the program is operating successfully, a highly skilled operator is not required. Several machines can be supervised at once.

Revise as you go!

- *What does CNC mean?*
- *Write down four advantages offered to the design team by CNC.*

CIM (Computer Integrated Manufacture)

Modern manufacturing industry uses computer technology to organise and control all aspects of the production process. CADD and CAM systems form part of computer integrated manufacture. Design development, production scheduling, machining operations, assembly and packaging can all be monitored using a single system as shown in the schematic diagram below.

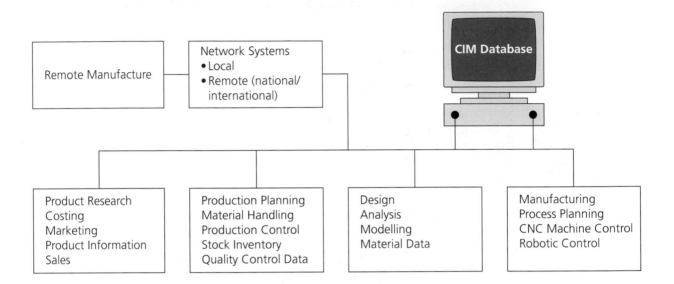

The diagram shows how the computers are linked together. Although they can perform their functions separately, they are also able to interact so that nothing is done in isolation. The software on the central computer manages the system.

Computer information can now be sent almost anywhere in the world in a matter of seconds. This enables the product to be made remotely from the source of data, i.e. to be made somewhere else.

The overall aim of CIM is to manufacture products at minimum cost in as short a time as possible. With this integrated approach being used at all stages there should be no divisions between the designers and manufacturing teams.

Advantages

Manufacturers who have adopted such systems have distinct advantages over their competitors.

- Data can be exchanged via computer links.
- The system operation can readily be checked using simulations of the program.
- The time taken to design and make products is significantly reduced.
- Quality and reliability have been dramatically improved.
- The cost savings can be passed on to customers via competitive pricing strategies. This is made possible by savings in time, materials and by reductions in labour costs.

To be competitive manufacturers have to be efficient. Lead times from initial idea to finished product are becoming shorter. As the market begins to demand more technologically advanced products manufacturers have to find ways of meeting this demand by improving their manufacturing and production methods. A computerised approach is the only way to deliver this improvement.

CIM systems are becoming more sophisticated. Information storage and retrieval is instantaneous. Manufacturing is almost totally controlled by intelligent computers, which operate CNC machines automatically. This removes the need for skilled operators. The overall quality of manufacturing is enhanced as these machines work with absolute precision.

CIM is an effective way of integrating CAD and CAM systems. CIM links the separate elements so that drawings produced on a CAD system can be automatically translated to machine code for CNC machining.

Revise as you go!

- *What is CIM an abbreviation of?*
- *List the advantages of CIM.*

Rapid Prototyping

Model-making has always been a vital part of product design and product development. Each model's purpose and usefulness may vary from a simple 2-dimensional, sketched model which explores visual form to a basic 3-dimensional model which allows functional qualities to be tested, or to a fully working prototype.

Making a useful model takes time and, in a competitive marketplace, companies continue to look for ways to cut development and manufacturing time to a minimum to allow their new products to be launched as early as possible.

The Process

'Rapid Prototyping' is a method of producing a 3-dimensional model or prototype quickly, direct from a 3-D computer drawing. It does not use any of the traditional model-making tools and can be described as 'clean manufacturing'. The process is very accurate and precise and enables the model maker to create intricate and complex forms. The process may also require traditional finishing and detailing to make up the actual prototype.

There are many different types of rapid prototyping used today but, in general, they can be grouped as follows:

- systems which use liquid resins which are solidified by a laser beam
- systems that melt and then fuse solid material
- systems which use a binder to connect the primary material.

Rapid prototyping begins with a design being drawn on 3-D CAD software. This drawing is then converted to a .STL file which is used to produce the model. A .STL file uses a network of triangles to represent the surfaces on a 3-D model and this '**Surface Triangulation Language'** is the standard format for rapid prototyping. There are many systems and machines available to produce the model but the principle is similar for all. The computer software examines the drawing and begins to recognise it as one 3-dimensional object. It then slices the product drawing into layers, each one being read by the rapid prototyping machine. The model is then produced layer by layer, sometimes using high precision lasers.

Stereolithography

Stereolithography is now one of the oldest types of rapid prototyping and has been in use since the mid 1980s. The process requires a photosensitive epoxy resin to be contained in a vat. Also inside this vat is a movable table which can be raised and lowered, allowing the resin to flow freely over and around it. The resin is used as the material to build the model. To start the process, the table is raised to just below the surface of the resin. The resin is solidified on top of the table by laser beams which are reflected onto the resin by movable mirrors. The table is then lowered by the equivalent of one layer before the lasers are used to solidify the next layer of resin.

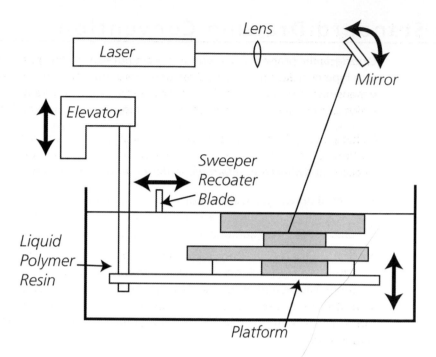

Other methods of rapid prototyping include:

Selective Laser Sintering (SLS) This process uses a wider range of materials e.g. polymers, metals and ceramics. The chosen material in powder form is rolled onto a platform and a laser sinters selected areas. The powder melts than hardens.

Fused Deposition Modelling (FDM) In this process a coil of ABS is fed through a heater, melted then extruded. The model is drawn one layer at a time by this molten filament. Each layer bonds to the one beneath.

3D printing (3DP) uses material in powder form in a similar way to SLS. A water based adhesive is printed using conventional ink-jet technology binding each layer together. Can also be used in earlier modelling stages.

Laminated Object Manufacturing (LOM) is now considered to be obsolete but is still widely used in industry. The model is built up in layers using a foil with an adhesive backing. Each layer of foil is pressed to the next using a heated roller and is then cut by a laser.

Revise as you go!

- *Explain the difference between a prototype and a model.*
- *What advantages does rapid prototyping have over traditional methods?*
- *Why is it vital that a prototype is made before a product is released onto the market?*

British Standard Drawing Conventions

Orthographic projection is used for working drawings ('ortho' means right or correct). This type of drawing conforms to codes and standards (conventions) which will be understood by the people involved in manufacturing. There are four main views: Plan, viewed from the top; and three separate Elevations, viewed from the front and both ends. Not all need be used to convey the information required, and a sensible selection of the most appropriate view(s) has to be made.

Working drawings are of two types: detail and assembly drawings.

- Detail drawings illustrate individual components and provide information on materials and how they are to be made. They outline the shape, show dimensions and provide any additional information on manufacture.
- Assembly drawings show how individual parts make a complete unit. They provide reference information on shape, position, relationship and identity of each part, and provide a parts list.

The basic elements of technical drawings are line, lettering, scale and dimensions.

Line Types

Outline
(firm and thick)

Construction
(faint and thin)

Hidden
(thin and dashed)

Centre line
(thin with long and short dashes)

Cutting plane
(arrow pointing to chain line)

Dimension line
(thin with neat arrow head pointing to leader line)

Section
(thin 45° equally spaced lines)

Break lines
(thick, drawn freehand)

Lettering

USE BLOCK LETTERING. Develop a consistent style of hand-drawn lettering. The size of text will depend on whether it is for notes, titles or headings.

Scale

Views are drawn proportional to the actual size.
For example:
The scale chosen depends on object size, paper size and the clarity required.

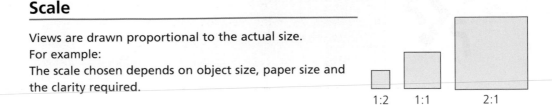

1:2   1:1   2:1

Dimensioning

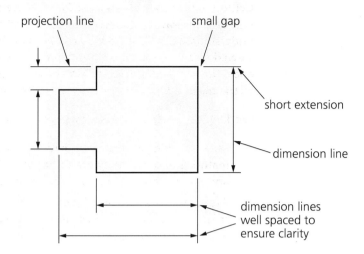

Every object has overall dimensions of length, width and height. Detailed dimensions are used to give information on sizes and locations.

The diagram (above) shows you how to set out dimension lines around a component drawing.

An example of a completed drawing, with dimensions, is shown below.

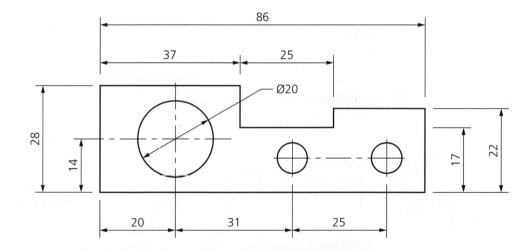

Case Study

Visit **www.roymech.co.uk** to get more information on British Standards drawing conventions. Write this web link in your file.

The photograph holder/storage box was designed and made by a pupil in response to a class assignment. Prior to manufacture she produced the drawings below.

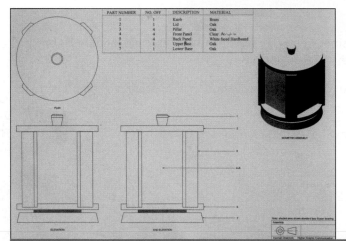

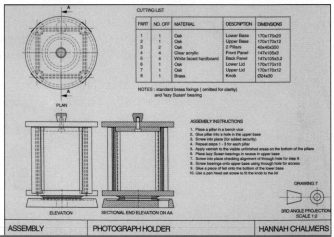

A working drawing which is drawn to scale can eliminate the need for many if not all dimensions. This leaves the drawing uncluttered and easy to read. This CAD drawing shown includes main sequencing and scheduling procedures.

Revise as you go!

- Describe two pieces of information that a manufacturer needs to find from an orthographic drawing of a product to ensure accurate alignment with other parts.
- What is a 'datum' surface?
- What information should be included in a parts list?